Wanted: Sensitive, intelligent, loving mate. Must enjoy outdoors, reading, music, quiet chats by the fireplace. I'm professional, goal oriented, attractive, loyal and loving. Wish to share the beauty of Alaska with adventuresome, fun-loving, reliable man looking to marry a choosy woman of the North. Send letter with photo.

Please address questions and book requests to: Harlequin Reader Service
U.S.: 3010 Walden Ave., P.O. Box 1325, Buffalo, NY 14269
Canadian: P.O. Box 609, Fort Erie, Ont. L2A 5X3

Wanted: Spouse

LOUELLA NELSON
MAIL-ORDER MATE

Harlequin Books

TORONTO • NEW YORK • LONDON
AMSTERDAM • PARIS • SYDNEY • HAMBURG
STOCKHOLM • ATHENS • TOKYO • MILAN
MADRID • WARSAW • BUDAPEST • AUCKLAND

HARLEQUIN BOOKS
225 Duncan Mill Road, Don Mills,
Ontario, Canada M3B 3K9

ISBN 0-373-30132-4

MAIL-ORDER MATE

Copyright © 1987 by Louella Nelson

Celebrity Wedding Certificates published by permission of
Donald Ray Pounders from *Celebrity Wedding Ceremonies*.

This edition published by arrangement with Harlequin Books S.A.

® and TM are trademarks of the publisher. Trademarks indicated with
® are registered in the United States Patent and Trademark Office, the
Canadian Trade Marks Office and in other countries.

Printed in U.S.A.

A Letter from the Author

Dear Friend,

Alaska gets in the blood. From my home in California, I'm delighted to share my passion for the southeastern panhandle region with you.

I've taken salmon alongside a grizzly bear fishing the same stream. I've run out of fuel in a small plane flying above glistening fjords. At the mouth of the great Taku River, I've "spent the night on the bar" in a small boat, awaiting the flood tide and the spectacular splash of dawn against glaciers on both banks of the river.

Enjoy similar adventures as my feisty heroine bends the rules in the ongoing Alaskan tradition of sending for a mail-order mate.

Then please write to me. I'd love to hear from you.

Go for your dreams!

Lou Nelson

To my Juneau brothers and sisters:
Johnny and Anna Marg Rear
John and Betty Lauritzen.
And to T.R.L.—choose life.

Prologue

Meau-ahh-agh! Meaugh!

Sue Ann McMillan Blackburn was picking blueberries when the unearthly moan tore through the rain forest.

Startled, she crushed a handful of berries against her buffalo-plaid shirt and spun around toward the road. Three hundred yards west through the woods, her two-year-old daughter, Serena, lay sleeping in the battered orange Chevrolet. The doors were locked, a window open an inch; Serena was safe, she reminded herself. In relief, she dragged in a lungful of musky air.

A quarter-mile to her left, the hiss of Montana Creek rose and fell. The water boiled around moss-covered logs and boulders, rushing and receding, muffling the cawing of ravens as they tore at the remains of spawned-out salmon.

Overhead, a bird whistled. Then a second moan hushed everything, and Sue Ann's heart hammered.

She was a green *cheechako*, a twenty-two-year-old newcomer to Alaska; in this moment, she felt her innocence of the wilderness, her fear of it, just as acutely as she'd felt her vulnerability in Los Angeles a few months ago. In that steel and concrete jungle her husband Bill had been murdered, and the brutal death had cracked her self-confidence. She noted how quick she was to tremble now.

Meaugh! the feral wail came again.

A series of banging noises, like stones thrown against a submerged tin can, warbled out of the woods near the creek. Dog? Hunter? Bear?

Bending to grasp the berry bucket, her only weapon, Sue Ann bolted.

She skirted a stand of spined devil's club, bounded over mountain fern and ducked under the bows of a spruce. The bucket swung wildly. Zigzagging left and right, she barreled down an incline, trying to keep her line toward the car reasonably straight. Dear God, she prayed, dear God.

Heart plunging like a piston, she charged into a small clearing.

Meaueau-ugh!

A brown blur and a flash of silver tumbled into the meadow.

Sue Ann plowed to a halt, half in shock, half in wonder. A bear cub the size of a Saint Bernard dog heaved upright and slashed at a square lard container wedged over his head. It looked as if his coffee-brown coat had been bleached in an area the size of a basketball, high on his left hip.

Suddenly the Alaskan brown grizzly dropped to all fours and rammed hard into a boulder. The twang of metal striking stone reverberated.

Still hyped with adrenaline, Sue Ann moved jerkily around the edge of the clearing, positioning herself between the cub's back and the gravel road, somewhere uphill.

She glanced into the shadows of the woods. The ferocity of mother bears was legendary. Thinking of the limited bear lore she knew, the horror stories of human maulings, blindness, terrible scars and death, she shuddered.

The cub wailed, and Sue Ann faced him. Groaning and growling, he clawed at the can. He tumbled to his back and scratched at the metal. His fur leaped with labored breathing.

Sue Ann felt helpless. The yearling cub would starve, or drown in the creek if he attempted to drink.

But she couldn't risk involvement. Her husband was dead, and that meant Serena would face life alone, like this cub, if something happened to her mother.

At the animal's next flurry of movement, Sue Ann dropped the berry bucket and took off uphill.

In seconds, brush snapped behind her. Some instinct in the bear had urged him to follow, although the tinny whacking of the can against trees and rocks told her his progress was difficult.

There was a period of silence during which Sue Ann broke out onto the road. Her breathing rasped and her hands shook as she dug into her jeans pocket for the keys. Spotting the faded orange paint job, she sprinted for it.

Serena lay sleeping in the back seat, her rosebud lips relaxed, her cheeks pink, and her small hands open on either side of her face. Black curls, so stark a contrast to Sue Ann's chaff-gold hair, lay like lace against her forehead. Her stained gray teddy bear lay on the floorboards.

Sue Ann's legs buckled in relief, and she gripped the car roof. Seconds passed. Her breathing slowed. Rubbing her damp face against a sleeve, she glanced toward the woods.

A sadness filled her. Babies were babies, whether animal or human. They were the reason for struggle in all of life. That cub would probably be wasted, and it was a shame, but Serena's security had to come first.

Back in town there might be help. Her eighteen-year-old brother Eric might be pried from his part-time job at the survey company, and with a gang of his friends—

But no, in two hours the cub would have wandered off into the forest.

Meaugh!

The bear charged out of the woods fifty feet beyond the car. He galloped up the roadbed, hesitated, bawled, and charged back down again. The youngster ran straight into the trunk of a fir tree. He teetered, staggered, fell down. Was he out cold? Had he suffocated? Sue Ann waited for five minutes, but he stayed down.

She glanced at Serena, at the inert cub, at her blueberry-stained hands, and once more at the still brown body of the bear.

Her decision made, she straightened up.

After retrieving her black cord jacket from the front seat, she shrugged into it, zipped the front, and took the tire iron with her. In seconds she was standing over the cub.

Thick rough fur glistened in the sunlight. Twigs and moss littered his back and legs. A right front paw lay beneath his chest, the other three legs stretched out from his body; one of the five toe pads on the left front paw was scored and bleeding. Sue Ann felt sympathy, but quelled it by noting the gleam of his claws.

She set the tire iron on the fir needles; it was handy as a weapon, but useless for pulling the can off the bear.

Then, taking a deep breath, she bent in front of the animal and forced her fingers inside the container, above and below his head. Tensing, she split her lips in a grimace and gave a mighty backward lunge.

The tin stayed in place but the cub came to with a snarl. He jerked away, wedging Sue Ann's fingers tight inside the can. *Please, no....* Her heart thundered. She twisted and yanked to get free. The bear cuffed at her arms. Three, four passes, and he'd slashed the corduroy without reaching her flesh.

A rock caught the heel of her boot and she fell, her face ramming into the bear's withers. He smelled like moldy mushrooms. He grasped her shoulders, and it felt as if the state of Alaska had wrapped its mighty arms around her in a death-hug. Iron locks of fear closed over her throat, squeezing her breath to ragged cries. They wrestled like gladiators, the cub bawling and slashing, Sue Ann trying to yank away.

Bill felt this way, she thought during the struggle. Incredulous, because death could come so ruthlessly. A whim, poor timing, a mistake in judgment—any of these could still breathing forever. Sue Ann understood how helpless he must have felt, how isolated. Dear God, for Serena's sake, she prayed.

Suddenly the bear's claws sliced like streaks of acid into her right forearm, and she screamed. Entangled in the fabric and flesh, enraged, he bellowed and swiveled, sinking his talons to the bone. His jaws snapped inside the can, sending terror deeper into Sue Ann's mind. Yet, with the razors of fire ripping her flesh, Sue Ann reacted instinctively to protect herself: she buried her face in the fur of his shoulder.

They fell against the fir tree, the container taking a tremendous whack. After a vacuumlike sound the can jerked free, banging to the ground. The impact put a foot of space between their faces. The bear panted, and Sue Ann could smell rotten fish. She moved slightly, and the sickles of pain slid from her arm. She sagged, moaning.

The bear let out a low cry.

Gathering her courage, she stilled her moans and met the stare of red-brown grizzly bear eyes.

She was stunned by the will to survive she saw there. An opaque, almost glassy look of surprise did not mask the glare of the wilderness beast. He would kill, and she saw the intent of it in the deadly stare.

In that moment Sue Ann felt an answering upsurge of power, and knew her eyes mirrored the glare of the survivalist. The time between recognition and challenge was nonexistent.

The yearling issued a confused murmur. Then he inched backward, swung down and gamboled into the brush.

Seconds passed. Instinct receded. Sue Ann's terror began to break up and fade. Still in shock, she looked at her right arm. A tattered sleeve . . . blood streaming from ugly gouges.

She gasped and began to shake. Cradling her arm, she heaved upright and stumbled toward the car, her mind reeling with disjointed thoughts.

She must never tempt fate. She could die.

She had experienced loneliness so profound it had bent her double sometimes, and death lurked on even the sunniest day in paradise. She must warn Serena. The world was full of dragons.

Chapter One

Sunset poured around the peaks of Douglas Island, radiated across Gastineau Channel, and burnished the face of Alaska's capital city. The snowbanks along Juneau's roads looked like a baker's arms reddened by the hearth. Behind the windows of a Subaru station wagon, the wavy wheat-gold hair of the driver danced with copper lights. The afterglow brushed her blue suit with magenta and softened the filigree of age around her eyes.

Sue Ann McMillan Blackburn circled Eagan Drive, named for a former governor of the forty-ninth state. The road wound along the perimeter of the city, tucking Juneau into the apron of the mountains. Mozart's twenty-fifth symphony played on the radio, but the notes barely reached Sue Ann as she shifted into neutral at a traffic light and rubbed absently at the right sleeve of her suit. It was a habit to rub the old bear scars. She caught herself, shook her head, and eased the Subaru along behind a Chevy pickup.

Worrying the ridges of tissue meant she was nervous. All right, she admitted, she was. She'd just taken a six-month leave of absence from her managerial position with the Department of Fisheries. If her recent gamble paid off, she wouldn't be returning, yet the gamble had put not just her job but every facet of her life at risk: her brother Eric's trust, her emotional security at the cabin, her career and attendant rise in Alaskan political circles. She was risking everything to marry a near-stranger, a man with whom she'd exchanged letters, phone calls and a videotape, but nothing else, not so much as a handshake.

She knew she was not immune from tragedy in this, her biggest gamble for happiness.

There was the matter of the letter postmarked Washington, D.C., for instance. That was a variable she'd never expected—having to keep such a momentous secret from her brother, as well as from her future mate. Nor could she have known how heavy a burden the secrecy would be, last January when the letter had arrived and she had decided to honor the terms of the trust. For she could tell no one about the legacy. To do so would void the terms of the inheritance. She must keep the contents of the letter to herself until after the wedding—or lose the $50,000 promised to her when she married.

Not since her daughter Serena's birth, twenty years earlier, had she felt such foreboding over her decisions.

Not only was Jerry Teal arriving tomorrow, but Eric, her Rock of Gibraltar for the entire time she'd been in Alaska, did not even know. She'd only told her brother—this morning—that she'd placed a Personals ad in the *L.A. Times*. He'd immediately demanded an audience, of course. She was grateful she'd waited till the last minute to tell him; as it was, she was already plagued with doubts about the wisdom of her actions. Yet the cabin out beyond Amalga Harbor echoed with loneliness....

Glancing ahead to the blue metal bridge spanning the channel, feeling the tension coil within, Sue Ann tried to review what she'd tell Eric. That she'd been engaged since July? He would be deeply hurt. And then angry. His temper would flare, and without meaning to, he'd retaliate. He'd want to know why she felt so high-and-mighty these days, not to need his advice anymore, not to choose one of his surveyor friends or any of the decent men in Alaska, where men far outnumbered women.

To substantiate her need to control the circumstances of her coming marriage, she would remind Eric of her devastating, sordid affair with Mark, the governor's financial advisor, ten years before. And Eric would scoff and say she was an idiot to think it could happen again. But he'd never convince her it couldn't. If there was one thing she'd learned in forty years of living, it was that if the joys waited out there for the person gutsy enough to go for them, so did the disappointments and sorrows and unrelenting pain. She had scars no one could see to prove it.

She'd brought only two people into her confidence: Viv, who was her beauty consultant and confidant and wouldn't give up a secret even under torture, and Serena, who'd been unable to come home this summer because she'd landed an internship at a prestigious interior-design firm in Seattle, and so had had to hear the news over the telephone last July.

Young and adventurous, Serena said she admired her mother's pluck in selecting a mate. Yet she was sensitive enough to understand Sue Ann was nervous.

"Don't be scared, Mama," Serena had told her yesterday on the phone as she rummaged around in a box of art supplies, looking for a drawing pencil she needed for class that morning. "You need someone special in your life. You deserve it. And Jerry sounds like a dream of a man. I can't wait to meet him. Until I get there, be brave, Mama. Go for the gusto."

Sue Ann took heart from the memory. Dammit, she had a right to "go for the gusto," she thought now, downshifting, braking, accelerating without really concentrating. She had a right to set up the rules, to eliminate potentials for failure and control all the variables in selecting a mate; she had a right to do so because she was forty, she'd been around the block, and she was scared.

By dint of the wintering she'd done in Alaska, she was considered a sourdough, an Alaskan with seasoning enough to survive the toughest challenges the state had to offer. And like the gold miners and pioneers who'd settled the Last Frontier, this past Christmas she'd gazed down the corridor of winters to come and had felt she had earned the right to exercise the old sourdough custom of marrying a mail-order mate.

Feeling more confident about facing Eric, Sue Ann turned onto the Douglas Bridge.

"YOU ACTUALLY PLACED an ad in the *Los Angeles Times*?" Eric called out the minute she stepped into the barn-style chalet.

Passing by the kitchen, Sue Ann grinned at Laura, her sister-in-law, whose forearms were dusted with flour, and went into the sunken living room. As she stepped down into the glass-lined conversation pit and tossed her purse on the couch, Eric pinned her with a stern look. "What the hell's gotten into you?"

"In front of your child," Sue Ann chided, her tone jaunty to hide her apprehension. She tousled the strawberry-blond curls of her seven-year-old niece, whose arms were wrapped around Eric's neck. "How're you, sprout?" she said.

"Fine. Daddy and I are having a wrestling match." Her tawny eyes twinkled. "Aunt Sue?"

"What?"

"Yesterday when you came over you had snow in your hair. You looked like Lady Diana. She married a prince. Daddy says you're not marrying any prince, that's for sure, but I told him you look like a princess anyway. An older princess."

Sue Ann's gaze swept to Eric's blooming cheeks. He'd been building a case without evidence. The brat. He'd done that to her for years.

His face was as red as the hands he circled around Tana to lift her to her feet. "Go give your mother a hand with the cookies, busybody," he said. He unfolded himself to nudge his daughter up the steps toward the kitchen.

A tall, rangy man with brown hair that fell in a shelf over his right temple, he wore a green plaid shirt and had the rough hands of a typical Southeast Alaskan outdoorsman. His hands were as red as a lobster fisherman's. At thirty-six, he ran his survey crews in the rain and biting winds, worked on his Taku River cabin while it was snowing, and skinned out deer when it was ten degrees above zero. But most of all, Eric's hands were raw from pursuing his real passions, boating and fishing. The rougher the weather, the more pride he took in hauling in a forty-seven-pound king salmon.

Sue Ann wished Eric had more of his wife's gentleness and understanding.

Eric noted her appraisal, and challenged her with an un-blinking blue-eyed stare. "You advertised for a husband, for crying out loud?" he said.

She gave him a level look. "That's right. I've been living in Alaska eighteen years, and I figure I've earned the right. It's an old custom here."

"You're not some lonely old pioneer, Sue. You've got looks, a career, a halfway decent personality." He frowned. "When you're not ordering everyone around, I mean. And a sensible head, usually. Why'd you put a stupid ad in the newspaper?"

"I'm forty," she said flatly. "At that age, it's hard to find a man who's right for marriage, Eric." Turning, she wandered to a gun cabinet set against a wall paved in fieldstone. How could she explain so he understood? Rubbing the cherrywood doorframe, she said, "I couldn't go through again what I went through the last time."

"Hell, the Juneau press corps gave you a bad time. So what? That was ten years ago, and the guy lost his job in the governor's office. He paid for his sordid little life-style. Life goes on."

The memory stabbed through her, but she calmed her features as she turned to look at him. "I guess I never really had my heart in the dating game after Mark. I was thinking of Bill, too."

"Sue Ann, that was almost two damned decades ago."

She winced at his rough manner. Memories of Bill were full of violence. Her husband had been murdered outside the Los Angeles Coliseum where he'd been attending a boxing match. She'd learned of his death the next morning in the newspaper. It had been ugly, but the pain had faded, and she could think of him with fondness. Mark was another matter.

Fighting impatience as she tried to reach the soft spot she knew Eric possessed, she chose her words carefully. "It's just that I lost so much when Bill died, Eric. Then the incident with the bear seemed to sap my confidence. It took years to build it back again, lonely, bitter years. And then Mark—that mess with Mark. They were awful years as far as personal relationships go. Years I couldn't have faced without your support. But, Eric—" she came to him, her voice warm "—everything in this world works in pairs: turtledoves, shoes, place settings at restaurants—have you ever noticed? Couples. I want the closeness you and Laura share. Try to understand. It can get lonely. I'm ready to chance this business of mating again, but I've got to do it my way. I've got to protect myself this time.''

Eric brushed the hair from his eyes, an impatient gesture. ''How can you expect to get anyone but a kook, placing an ad like that? Especially in L.A. You know from losing Bill what that city is like. Killers. Thugs. Indigents. Cutthroat businessmen.''

She shuddered. ''They're not *all* like that. Besides, give me more credit. I'm not going to marry anybody like that.''

''You made a mistake with that governor's aide,'' he reminded her.

She glanced out the window at the slate-gray channel, clinging to control. Bits of snow softened the view. Why couldn't Eric soften? He was being bullheaded; worse than usual. *Dear God, give me the words....*

''I tried to warn you,'' he continued, ''but you were in love. Blind to his shenanigans. Why can't you just have a normal courtship like me and Laura? Why can't you get serious with one of the guys here in town? The ratio of men to women must be twenty to one.''

She turned toward him. ''I *can't*, Eric.''

''Why the hell not? Single life is a chance to make choices. Reasonable choices.''

''Choices like John?'' she shot back.

Unperturbed, he shrugged. ''You could do worse than John. I'm putting him in charge of that mine-survey contract we're expecting in a couple weeks. Biggest job we've ever had. John's moving up.''

''He likes his beer. He belches.''

''So do I.''

''Yes, Eric, but you'd just introduced us thirty seconds earlier. It was crass. And he's never read so much as a best-seller, let alone a classic.'' She shook her head. ''I'd be bored with him.''

''Admit it, the real hitch is that you couldn't run him around just as you pleased. He's a man's man. Do you always have to run things? A wife's place is—''

"Eric, for the love of God! You're deliberately picking a fight." She stalked to the sofa, turned around and faced him. "I do not order everyone around."

"Yes, you do. You're always organizing things. Everything. Every detail."

"Like when?"

"My company picnic."

"Why, you ungrateful—" She needed Eric's understanding, and once more she checked her anger, gentled her tone. "You love soccer and baseball and badminton. You loved seeing the wives jump around in those gunnysacks. You said so."

"I didn't like the pace you set. We weren't out to compete in the decathlon or anything. Nobody had time to relax."

Hurt, she paced to the plate-glass window. Her cheeks felt as hot as the sun that had faded at dusk. Damn him. He was going to wage the Civil War over the ad she'd placed just because she hadn't consulted him first. It angered her, his protectiveness. The force of it always caught her off guard. But she choked back the anger because Eric's acceptance of her plans was crucial to her happiness. She didn't want to have to choose between the two most important men in her future, and her first loyalty would have to lie with Jerry.

She would simply have to tell Eric her decision had been made, she decided, facing him again.

He'd gone to the liquor cabinet. "Drink?" he said, pulling open a door.

Maybe he was mellowing. Trying to. "All right," she said. "Harvey's."

Bottles clinked. Sue Ann walked to the couch, eyeing the brown tweed cushions. But she did not sit down. Tonight's confrontation required her to be alert. She'd barely touch her sherry, she decided. She wanted to convince Eric that Jerry would make her happy.

Sue Ann stared through the northwest window at the red-and-yellow blurs cast by the lights of homes and government buildings in Juneau, and her brows furrowed with worry. She'd kept another big secret from Eric—the same secret she had to keep from Jerry.

She'd done some thinking about the origins of the inheritance. After Bill's funeral, Eric had gone back to Juneau to take semester exams, and their Aunt Ester from Seattle had rushed to Los Angeles to help get Sue Ann packed up for the move north. She and Ester had remained close. According to her letters, Ester's own marriage late in life had brought her a happiness she'd wanted for Sue Ann. Certainly it was Ester who'd left her the money.

But why did she have the feeling her silence was putting at risk the trust of those she cared about most? Would Jerry think she'd chosen the first man to respond to her ad, just to get the money?

If only Eric could be brought to understand her need to control the circumstances in selecting a mate, then, when he accepted Jerry into the family, he might just reassure him that she was honorable.

Sue Ann rubbed her temples. It was only her weariness, dredging up insecurities she could easily squelch on a crisp morning at the cabin.

The cabin...she and Jerry, filling her isolated haven with laughter, maybe even with love....

Thinking of the physical impression he'd made last June, when they'd exchanged videotapes, she smiled.

From the moment she'd watched his image moving from desk to window to telephone as he'd shown her his office, she'd nicknamed him "the Harrison Ford of the financial world." It fit. Except for his cathedral-arch hairline, he didn't look much like the stereotypical accountant. Jerry wore the casual, elegant clothes of a fast-lane lover, walked like a man sure of his body, and slid from jokes to descriptions of complex corporate mergers with the facility of a crack government investigator.

It was incredible, but he'd even made love to her long-distance. He'd spoken softly of having talks before her fireplace. Potbellied stove, she'd corrected him, not fireplace—and they'd laughed about the error she'd made in the ad. He'd asked about Serena, and had listened as she'd described her daughter at age eleven, crying as she'd turned loose an orphaned deer she'd fostered. Sue Ann had asked about his work. She'd heard the frustration in Jerry's voice over a tax service he'd performed for a rude client, had understood his longing to be free of the professional grind, had coveted his eagerness to be with her—and had felt joy. The burr of his baritone voice on the telephone had sent electric energy spiraling from her heart to her womb.

He also had a childlike quality, she recalled, thrilled by his memory. Jerry Teal had a sparkle in his eyes that she'd seen in children who'd been playing ball for two hours.

She looked forward to the fun, the depth of intellectual exchange, and the promise of passion she saw in him.

And, except for the bear scars, she was proud of her appearance, eager to watch his expression tomorrow afternoon when he saw her for the first time. She knew she was a tall, striking woman. Eric called it "looks," but some of her male friends joked that they couldn't wait till the summer soccer season when she wore shorts. Jerry wouldn't be disappointed.

Thinking of the scars, she wondered why he hadn't mentioned them after she'd written—

"How's the training of the new gal coming along?"

At the sound of Eric's voice, she started slightly and turned around. She took the goblet of amber liquid he held out to her. "What?"

"The new gal you trained." Eric toasted her, and they drank. "How's she look to you? Fill your shoes okay?"

"Oh, yes. Fine. She's bright, conscientious. I think she can handle the department for six months."

"Six months?"

"I thought I'd mentioned—"

"*Six months?* Good God." Eric moved closer and stood in front of her, his face flushed. "Now your career will be shot."

"I've got seniority," she said archly. "Considering the needs of the fishermen, the Governor's office and the Canadian Fisheries people—after eight years of running things to everyone's satisfaction, I'm certainly entitled to a leave of absence and my job back in the spring if I want it."

"'If?' You're thinking of quitting?"

"I haven't decided."

"What about Serena's tuition? Is she going to have to go to work to stay in college?"

"It's taken care of," she said quickly—perhaps too quickly. Sue Ann took her time tasting the sweet sherry. He would not bully her into revealing the inheritance.

To cover the awkward pause, she leaned forward, squeezed his arm, let it go. "Not to worry," she said. "You pegged me correctly a while ago. Everything's in perfect alignment, just like the wheels on my car."

Shaking his head in disgust, Eric set his drink on the end table and picked up his briar pipe. The bit looked as though it had been gnawed by a beaver. He clamped it between his teeth.

The pipe unlit, Eric sat down on the couch. He bared teeth as perfect as Sue Ann's. "Why do I get the feeling this plan of yours is a fait accompli?"

Her mouth went dry. Suddenly ashen, Sue Ann sank into the cushions. She glanced at him. "The deed is done, Eric."

He jabbed at the air with his pipe. "You can still cancel the ad."

"It's far too late for that."

"Don't answer the letters you get."

"I've answered them."

He tensed. "Just when did you place this ad?"

"Months ago."

His eyes darkened to violet. He felt betrayed, and it wrenched her. She regretted having to hurt him with the rest. Setting her sherry on the carpet against the couch, she faced him and said softly, "Eric, my husband-to-be arrives tomorrow. His name is Jerry Teal."

Seconds passed while their gazes locked. Then, "I see." He rose, set the pipe on the table, stood looking down at it, his back to her.

"I know I didn't meet my mate in church, like you met Laura," she said, "but Jerry's a fun-loving, kind man. More importantly, I sense a strength in him. He's got a broad-shouldered approach to life, as if nothing were too terrible to face. The strength of character, the humor—it's a wonderful combination, Eric. He'll be right for me. You'll see."

"What about love, Sue Ann?" His voice sounded hollow.

"Love?"

He jerked around. His face hurt her. It looked as if someone had stretched canvas over a mannequin. "Love," he said harshly. "You know. The stuff women are supposed to go gaga over. You behave as if marriage were nothing more than a new job."

Laura rattled her baking pans, the timing perfect but the diversion wasted.

Sue Ann stood up, trembling. "I'm not some mercenary woman who wants to snare a man to pay her bills. I'm not after a protector, a replacement for you, either. Jerry and I are beautifully matched. We'll be friends, companions. I expect love to come to us."

"If he's so great, why didn't you mention him before? Is he an alcoholic? A womanizer? A gold digger?"

She stiffened. "You know very well Dad and Mom lost everything before the boating accident. I have no fortune." But guilt sped through her about the untold secret.

He seemed not to notice. He exhaled sharply. "The boating accident. You needed me then, to get through it. Just as you needed me when that football jock stood you up the night of your first high school dance. Like you always needed me, Sue Ann. And I was always there. Now—" anger tinted his features pink "—you make a mockery of the years we've spent helping each other reckon with the world."

"Eric—"

"Is there some reason you've kept this from me? Some embarrassment—" he waved searchingly "—some personality quirk, handicap, what?"

"No, Jerry's as sound as you and I. He's forty-five and strong-looking. He loves fishing, boating. He's looking forward to hunting with you and the guys before the wedding. We've got eight weeks—" She broke off and looked away.

"Got that planned already, too, huh? Fine, great. You're so organized, Sue Ann, you're a one-person army." He chopped the air. "Well, go ahead. Plan your precious wedding. I expect to be in the mountains on that mine project, anyway. Be sure to schedule the big event then, because I'm not coming to it."

He stalked across the living room and up the stairs. She followed, grabbed his arm, pulled until he turned around.

"Eric, don't do this," she ground out, tears misting her eyes. "You were practically Serena's father. My confessor, my friend, my old rock. Don't split us like this."

"You're the one who split us, Sue Ann." He jerked away. "Now you're on your own."

He walked down the hall to the coatrack, shrugged into his green ski jacket.

"All right," she called, her voice thick. "You can see the reason I never told you. Look at you, throwing a fit because my plans don't meet with your approval. Judging a man you haven't even met! You're a narrow-minded, overbearing redneck, and I don't want you meddling in my life anymore."

The door banged shut behind him.

Running to the couch, she grabbed her purse, climbed to the landing and hurried into her own coat, her stomach churning. "I'm leaving, Laura," she called, and turned away before her sister-in-law could respond.

She pulled open the door to a gust of wind and ducked down the porch stairs. Driven snow bit her face. Ahead, Eric was just passing through a beam of light from the kitchen window, reminding her of a little soldier in one of those glass paperweights filled with swirling snow.

Running to catch up, she shouted at him, "You don't have to stalk out of the house like an enraged husband, because I'm leaving!"

She passed him, reached the top of the hill a few seconds ahead of him, and spun around. "You're angry because I did this on my own. Well, I'm allowed, damn you. I do lots of things on my own, and it burns you up, doesn't it? Because you need to feel like a hero all the time."

She dug for her keys.

"Hero, hell." Eric puffed up to her and stood there in the dark, growling like a bear. "Hero? Is that what you call someone who bails you out of jams and watches your kid while you gallivant off to Anchorage and Canada and the States?"

"Gallivant?" She pushed her face up close to his. "Those were management seminars and business trips, not pleasure forays! But after twenty years of work I think it's about time I thought of myself for a change. From now on there'll be plenty of pleasure. I'll *wallow* in it. I'll be a regular hedonist. And I won't be asking permission from you!"

Jamming the key into the lock, Sue Ann opened the car and slid into it, forcing the key into the ignition. She fired the engine, pulling out fast, and the tires spun, spraying Eric with snow.

Chapter Two

Sue Ann disliked crowds, disliked them intensely. Crowds of people, especially at airports where the emotions were raw, shredded her composure and snatched away the order in her life.

At this moment, she felt scattered. The weeks of expectancy, the fight with Eric, and now this six-hour delay in the teeming airport lounge had robbed her of her dignity. She would not look fresh and self-contained for Jerry now. She'd look red-cheeked and frayed at the edges.

As she tried again to search within for patience, someone bumped her shoulder. She jerked around.

A man wearing rubber boots and a bristly beard threw her an apology.

Shaking her head, Sue Ann faced forward. A woman carrying a crying baby chattered in her ear. Another held a salmon wrapped in newsprint that filled her nostrils with a scent like sour milk. They pressed around her, confounding her anxious focus on the arrival gate for Flight 69 from Seattle, the transfer from L.A.

When had "ten minutes to arrival" ever felt more like a century? She tugged at the edge of her white cable-knit sweater, adjusted the cowl collar, straightened the crimson scarf she'd told Jerry to look for. Still waging a battle against impatience, she took a couple of deep breaths. She gazed at the night-blackened windows lining the lounge. Outside, occasional bits of snow appeared like ballet dancers falling past the dark eaves into the radiance shining from the interior of the lobby. At least the snow had eased up.

Suddenly twin red lights arched through the darkness, a jet engine screamed, and the tedium of the six-hour wait vanished. Her heart revved and leveled off at just under the speed of a jackhammer.

The steamy crowd nudged Sue Ann forward. She tried to grip the mauve carpet with the tread of her boots, feeling panic, feeling her freedom slip away in the kaleidoscope of seconds before her future husband gripped her elbow and said—what?—"You're Sue Ann? Nice weather you have here." A joker, he'd begin with something light, because he loved to laugh. And she'd say—"You must be Jerry. Welcome to Juneau." Inane things, stiff things; the polite, strained chatter of lovers who'd never set eyes on each other.

Suddenly the situation was absurd. She'd made a mistake. She was too serious for Jerry's happy-go-lucky temperament. He would be bored in a week. Or she would lose patience with his carefree spirit. Eric was right: this was all wrong, marrying a man she barely knew. Couldn't she pray, quickly, for another delay while she gathered her confidence like a cloak around her frozen composure?

She wanted Eric beside her to steady her legs. She'd decided this morning that, although the rift hurt her, she needed a few days alone with Jerry to establish a bond. She wished now she'd called Eric, tried to patch the quarrel.

At this propitious second, she saw Jerry's grin of recognition.

The Harrison Ford image from the videotape came to life in the form of a tall man whose shoulders looked sturdy enough to hoist a moose, rather than the maroon canvas sports bag he carried. And his face—bold lean lines, a prominent chin softened by a cleft, crow's-feet that lent him seasoning, not age. Even as she remembered the risks she'd taken to bring this man into her life, she realized that the biggest one lay ahead. If she gave her heart and he misused it, she would be unable to trust her judgment again.

Yet, during the brief silent assessment they gave each other, his gaze changed the course of her thoughts. The gray-green color of his eyes reminded her of a lake shadowed by evergreens. There were undercurrents of excitement there. Complex depths. The hue was intensified by tastefully chosen clothes: a gray wool sport coat and a blending of gray, green and black in his tie. His dark slacks gave him a whipcord look and at the same time complemented the gunmetal-gray hair that framed his fine intelligent brow.

Her man, she thought with pride. Her bridegroom—a knockout in his own right. Did she measure up?

Running a quick hand through her hair, she lifted and settled the blond waves over her shoulders.

Jerry's gaze traveled from her hair down over her figure—lingering, savoring—and returned with admiration to her face. She felt an unexpected heat spiral through her. Her womanhood wouldn't be wasted on him. Then, abruptly, his wide mouth curved upward in pleasure.

It was the most stunning moment in memory. An energy suffused them like a halo, closing the distance of several feet between them to two at most and bonding them, moving them so deeply they both laughed aloud.

IF THERE WAS one quality Jerry Teal looked for in a woman, it was the ability to laugh, and she was laughing. She was radiant. Sue Ann McMillan Blackburn's smile made her glow from her wavy blond hair to her booted feet. His future bride had strength and self-command, but her magnetism was expansive, too, and he sensed the warmth of her nature. She was sharing that warmth with him now.

Delighted, he chuckled. "You're like the Alaska I remember from my Coast Guard days. Awe-inspiring."

Her cheeks were already pink, and they darkened. "It's not what I thought you'd say," she said.

"What did you expect?"

"Something funny."

"Only if the flight hadn't been delayed. Back about two o'clock, I could have dreamed up something more entertaining. Now..." He shrugged.

"Now you're exhausted." She came to his side, took his arm and propelled him past a group of high school kids pounding each other on the back and embracing. Why hadn't he thought to hug Sue Ann? He'd missed a golden opportunity to show her how glad he was finally to be with her.

She was taller than he'd expected: she came up past his shoulder, and he was six-one. Being tall, she could look more directly at him than the other women he'd dated. Set wide above high cheekbones, her eyes were the color of the California sky on a blustery spring day, a blue that reached all the way to space. As she guided him downstairs toward the baggage-claim area, he watched her gaze play over his features.

"Was it a tedious flight, Jerry?"

How good his name sounded coming from her. "One stop in Seattle," he said. "They held us there while you all had your snowstorm."

Sue Ann gave him a challenging glance that went directly to his gut. He'd put personal pronouns on the snowstorm and she had remarked on it. He liked her sensitivity. She listened.

"Sorry you had to wait," he offered.

"It happens here all the time. Snow or fog. Sometimes when the legislature is supposed to convene, it'll be socked in for ten days straight. When that happens, the people who've been fighting to move the capital up north get vocal again. It's easier to get in and out of Anchorage. The weather plays a major role in the lives of Southeast Alaskans."

Again that look of challenge. It almost said, Will you melt in a snowstorm? Her spirit made his pulse jerk.

"I'm looking forward to it," he said.

"What, the weather?" She let go of his arm and moved in front of him to traverse a bottleneck around the baggage belt. From over her shoulder, she scanned his face. "You're looking forward to the weather?"

"No, life here. It's the last word on the real meaning of freedom."

She responded with a quick, frozen smile that made his own fade. Then she turned away, her hair curtaining her expression.

They were both tense, he realized. Nothing satisfying could possibly come of trying to get to know her in the maelstrom of this airport.

He craned over some heads, spotted one of his steamer trunks, and eased himself up close enough to haul it off the belt. When he lifted the second one, Sue Ann shot him a look of surprise. In fifteen minutes he amassed a small mountain of trunks and suitcases.

Sue Ann glanced from them to his face. "I'm afraid we'll have to hire a cab after all," she said. "My Subaru won't fit all this. I thought you were going to ship most of your things by ferry."

He grinned. "These are just the things I thought I'd need right away."

"What's it like when you go on vacation?"

"A lot of bellhops get rich."

"I believe it." A smile softening the remote aspect of her high cheekbones and forehead, she inventoried his bags again. "Which are the important ones? We'll take those with us to the hotel."

He touched her arm. "Hotel?"

"The Breakwater Inn. I've been back twice to make sure they gave you a room overlooking Gastineau Channel. I'm sure you'll like—" Then she caught his surprise and disappointment. "Jerry—surely you didn't expect . . . I mean, until the wedding . . ."

Struggling with fatigue and disappointment, he shrugged, rubbed his jaw, glanced sideways at her. "Could we move the wedding up to tomorrow by any chance?"

"Why, no, the invitations—" Looking at him with new respect, she laughed. "I should have remembered. You're quick on your feet. I mustn't let down my guard."

"Could be interesting if you did."

"Mmm. You're very eager, aren't you? Or are you just better than me at covering up a case of nerves?"

As he reached for one of his bags and hefted the strap over his shoulder, a smile played over his mouth. Oh, she was a sensitive one, he thought. "I presume our sleigh awaits?" he said, keeping it casual.

She chuckled. "Quick on your feet and evasive into the bargain. I really must keep on my toes." She took a suitcase and stepped toward the exit. "This way, Jerry. Skycaps are in short supply in an airport this small, so we're on our own."

She was not going to be easy to get close to, he thought, easing up beside her to open the door with his shoulder. The challenge intrigued him.

An icy wind whipped into his face, smelling of the mountains and the incoming tide. Braced up by the wild night and the spirited woman he'd come to marry, he began to look forward to letting his Romeo heart out of its cage. He could send her flowers, dream up profound, loving things to woo her, kiss her until she was breathless, and leave her to think about how badly she wanted him. She'd been right, he was eager. A little rusty, perhaps, but the creative juices were beginning to flow. It had something to do with seeing her in person.

He watched her stride across the parking lot, her boots scuffing up clouds of snow, her face lifted to the wind. She was strong both mentally and physically. It was good to have a fighter beside him in a country like this. Smart to align himself with a survivor. And damned exciting, considering the chill of the nights, to have a woman who looked like she did in a sweater and jeans. Yeah, he was a lucky man. From now on, life was going to be fun.

Forty-five minutes later, they stood in front of a picture window in the softly lit hotel room, gazing into a blizzard.

Jerry watched Sue Ann's reflection in the glass as she pointed into the whiteness. "You'll see it in the morning. Out there, the Juneau/Douglas Bridge connects the mainland with Douglas Island. On this side of the bridge, you'll see the masts of the salmon trollers in Aurora Boat Harbor." Her knit sleeve moved left. "My brother Eric lives over there, just a little this side of Douglas's boat harbor and Sandy Beach. After you told me you loved rugged country, I knew the Breakwater was the place for you. It'll be gorgeous when the snow stops. Douglas Island is a mass of mountains."

"It was nice of you to take the trouble, Sue Ann. Really."

"No trouble." She gave him a half glance. "I thought about Eric's place. He's got the loft room with a view of the channel. But it wouldn't have been as . . . peaceful."

"Naturally not, what with Tana and all her little school chums running about. They would have been kind of cute, but we have more privacy here."

"Mmm," she murmured.

Perhaps she was shy, he thought. He wondered how long it had been since she'd— But it was none of his business. Her past personal life was a private matter, just as his was.

For now, he would take things slowly, giving her a chance to gain a little more confidence in him. He enjoyed her low voice, and her perfume reminded him of daffodils, crisp yellow flutes of sunshine growing on a mountain slope. Wanting to stay close to her in this cocoon they'd created just this side of the snowstorm, he gestured, "Do they ski up there?"

"Right along with the jackrabbits and bear." She absently rubbed her arm. "Do you ski?"

"A few years back I took five days off and drove to Mammoth Mountain."

"Oh, yes," she said, as if she knew right where it was.

"I was an intermediate skier by the end of the week, but I wouldn't run any downhill races tomorrow. How about you?"

"I don't get up on the slopes very often, either. There's something a little crazy about hurtling down a mountain." She turned, looked into his eyes. "Something, I don't know... reckless about it."

Her comment seemed at odds with the purposeful way she strode through a snowstorm. "How's that?" he asked, wanting to keep her talking.

Before she could explain, someone knocked on the door.

"Must be the other bags," he said, crossing to open it. A hotel official in a dark suit stood outside. His forehead gleamed in the hall light. Beside him, a silver champagne bucket, wax tapers in silver holders and trays of sandwiches and fruit covered a wheeled cart.

The man checked a ticket in his hand and looked up. "Mr. Teal?"

"Yes, what's this?" Jerry glanced over his shoulder and saw Sue Ann's smile.

"My welcome surprise," she said, going to the table near the window. She motioned, and Jerry stood aside as the waiter wheeled in the cart and draped the table in white linen. He set out the refreshments, lit the candles, and poured champagne into the two goblets. Then he said gravely, "Enjoy, sir. Miss, have a good evening."

Jerry reached into his jacket for his wallet.

The waiter shook his head. "It's taken care of, sir. Good night." He let himself out.

Jerry turned to Sue Ann. Lifting both glasses, she held one out in his direction.

He took it. "Talk about being quick on your feet. This was a very smooth move."

She winked. "There are benefits to being organized."

"I'll say." He studied her a moment, letting the pleasure sweep over him. "You're a romantic, aren't you, Sue Ann?"

"Would you consider it a plus if I were?"

"Definitely."

"Well, then," she said. "'She had been forced into prudence in her youth, she learned romance as she grew older.' A little something from Jane Austen to answer your question." Memory seemed to shadow her eyes. But she came back to him, looking up brightly, lifting her glass. "Let's drink to romance, Jerry."

They toasted, drank. Jerry felt his own memories stir, felt a small rise of old resentments. "My favorite quote's from *My Fair Lady*. Didn't you say you like plays and musicals?"

"I haven't seen many, but I loved *Evita*. What's your quote? Does it give great insight into your personality?"

"You decide." He raised the stemware, touching it to hers. Sue Ann stared intently at him, her lips parted expectantly. "Here it is, then," he said. "'Pleasure without joy is as hollow as passion without tenderness.'"

"That's beautiful."

"I didn't write it."

"No, but you remembered it. And it's so sensitive. You're sensitive, Jerry."

"Ah, yes," he said dryly. "And quick on my feet, don't forget. I'd make a good song-and-dance man."

She laughed. "To pleasure with joy, then. And passion with tenderness."

"To having a good time," he echoed in a husky voice, wanting to caress her long wavy hair, take her in his arms.

They tilted their glasses, and afterward she stared at him. "You're going all serious on me, Jerry."

"Not really." He set down the glass.

"Most people like to have a good time. You're making a point of telling me. Why?"

"You're perceptive," he said. Walking to the rose-print coverlet on the king-size bed, he looked down at it. "Most people talk a good story, Sue Ann. I mean it."

She came to stand behind him. "Exactly what do you mean?"

"Nothing to alarm you. Just—" He turned and stood with a leg bent, attempting casualness. "I've worked a lot of fourteen-hour days in the past eighteen or twenty years. It cost me a lot personally." He couldn't tell her that people's account books were safer territory than dealing with their emotions. He shrugged. "I'm not sorry. Things worked out. But I hustled to fill my calendar, and when I was working weekends and holidays, my clients had a six-week wait to get in. Years of corporate mergers and investment portfolios and limited partnerships, until I saw P and L's and financial agreements in my sleep. And then, as I was gulping black coffee before going to the office one Sunday morning, I saw your ad."

He stopped, looked around. The baggage was stowed neatly in the closet, the beige carpet and tan-and-rose appointments of the suite were well-chosen to soothe the weary traveler, and the view promised to be moving. Everything had been selected and arranged with care, even to the champagne and sandwiches. He was a lucky man, dammit. He was a burned-out businessman who'd lost a wife because he'd been too busy to think of her needs. But he'd sold the business, so what was he worried about this time around? He looked at the woman who held his future happiness in her capable hands and saw that she was gazing at him with a light in her blue eyes. His heart did a dance step.

He reached out, ran his thumb gently along her jaw. Not a flicker in her gaze. He felt heat spark to life within him, felt a crazy urge to kiss her mouth. Instead, he caressed her lower lip. Then he slid his hand into his sport-coat pocket and made a fist. He wouldn't rush things, he thought. This was too important.

In a hushed voice, she said, "What happened when you saw the ad?"

"I didn't go to the office."

She let that be its own significant fact. "What did you do?"

"I went out and got drunk."

"Why?"

He smiled. "I like to have a good time."

"Somehow I wish I could quote something profound to you about understanding. But I'm not sure I understand what you really mean by having a good time. Had it been a while?"

He nodded.

"Then what happened?"

"Then I wrote you a letter."

Her eyes widened. "You wrote that wonderfully touching letter while you were inebriated?"

He nodded.

"Well, still, it was in you, I suppose. The feelings were your own."

"Yes, they were my own."

"Next you sent the telegram," she persisted.

"No, Monday I told my partner I was selling my half of Teal & Moss Financial Services. Gave him first option to buy."

"Even before I'd answered your letter, Jerry? Are you normally so impulsive?"

"When I want something very much. Twenty years is a long time to want something very much."

"Oh, yes, twenty years is a long time." A silence stretched between them. "Still, it's incredible. It was in June that you described the sale of the business. I had no idea it had occurred so suddenly. I don't know where you got the guts to do something that crazy." Her mouth contracted in an attempt to contain an emotion he didn't understand. In a move to get past the moment, she picked up the glasses and offered his to him. "More champagne? It's California's best."

He went to her, looked into her eyes for a moment, trying to fathom where she went every time she got quiet. He took a drink. "Your ad wasn't exactly your everyday entrée to the dating scene."

She pushed some spilled grapes back onto the platter of fruit. "It was something I wanted very much—your being here." She looked briefly at him and walked to the window. "There's where we differ, I expect."

"How so?"

"My research told me arranged introductions had lost the stigma they used to have. Video dating services are doing a booming business in love these days." She glanced at him, responded to his wry smile by waving at him. "Really," she said. "Singles clubs draw people together for skiing, dancing and other common interests. I expect it has to do with the breakdown in the family unit and traditional values, don't you?"

"I never thought about it. The world does seem to be going to Hades in a handbasket. At least in L.A."

This time she didn't respond to his humor, but stared seriously at him. "Well, these other methods are working, filling the gap for a lot of lost souls, but they weren't for me."

"Why not?"

"Too—" she shrugged, turned away "—chancy, I guess. I decided to try advertising in the Personals column. It's one of the oldest methods in the book. The point is, I conducted a campaign to find you, Jerry. I planned every step, every word in the ad, every response to the responses I would get, every detail. It was so important, you see, not to leave anything to chance."

When she looked over her shoulder at him, her eyes pleaded with him, but her back was rigid with pride. He knew then what it had cost her to place the ad. Yet it made no sense, never had. Why would a woman with her class, looks and intelligence need to advertise to find a mate? Especially in Alaska, where women were said to be in short supply?

She faced the snowstorm. Her voice echoing softly against the window, she asked, "What are you thinking?"

"How lucky we are to have gotten what we wanted. Sue Ann?"

She moved back to the table and stood beside him, gazing into his face, searching it.

He gestured with his glass. "I think it's a plus that you organized this so well. I've had a lifetime of schedules and being organized. I find the thought of planning much at all, right now, a royal pain. You don't seem to mind it."

"It's the way I am."

"Good." He reached into his breast pocket for his wallet. Opening it, he withdrew a check and replaced the billfold.

"Yesterday I closed a couple of my bank accounts. Do you have any objections to handling the family finances?"

"But you're an accountant," she said. "I thought you'd be pretty particular about that end of things. I was willing to let you."

"I hate it. Do you?"

"Not at all. I rather like the exercise of balancing a checkbook. Helps me know the world is still turning, if you know what I mean."

Elated, he grinned, holding out the check. "This is a match made in heaven, Sue Ann. It's not the whole ball of wax, but this money should tide us over till spring anyway."

She took the bank draft, opened and glanced at it, folded the paper and moved as if to slip it into her jeans. Then she snapped it open again in front of her nose. "Holy mackerel!"

He laughed.

"Two hundred fifty thousand dollars. Jerry, I can't accept this." She handed it to him.

He curled her fingers around the check, pushed it away. "C'mon, now, Sue Ann. You're ruining that old cliché about a woman taking a man for everything he's got, for better or for worse."

"You've mixed your metaphors with your marriage vows. Jerry, this is insane. I can't let you. We agreed to pool our money fifty-fifty. My financial situation is fine, more than fine, but I can't match this. Not even close."

"Fifty-fifty was your offer. We never agreed."

"You never argued. I assumed . . ."

He set the check and the glass of champagne on the table and took her hands. He felt a quick rise of inward heat at touching her, but he willed it down and made her look at him. "Sue Ann, this isn't a temporary arrangement for me. This is my life, my dream: fun, travel, sharing my money with a good woman, jokes and walks in the woods, paddling around on our own Golden Pond. I want to share it. I want to share the Sunday paper with you and have quiet talks in front of the fireplace, like you said in your ad."

"Potbellied stove."

"Whatever. Do you want those things or not?"

"Of course, but you don't know me yet. I can't—"

"'Can't' isn't in our vocabulary anymore. Gone. Do you think over this past year of phone calls, letters and videotapes that I haven't noticed your warmth, your loneliness for your daughter, your sincerity, your loyalty to your brother Eric? That I would have missed, somehow, your ability to organize, your honesty about your faults, your temerity in learning mine?"

Her cheeks were beginning to blush, but her gaze was steady and quiet, as if she'd waited a lifetime to hear him speak. And somehow her strength had that uncanny ability to arouse him. A slight hesitation in his voice was the remnant of the struggle he made to stick to the point. "Do you know what's exciting?" he asked, shaking her hands a little.

She shook her head.

"What's exciting is that neither of us has yet revealed the inner self."

Her gaze slanted away.

He tilted up her chin. "You don't learn the depth of a person's character, the way I want to know yours, in a few months or a handful of years. It takes a lifetime. That's all before us, Sue Ann."

"How can you be so sure of everything, Jerry? You made your decision based simply on my ad."

He made an impatient sound. Then, in an aside, as if he were speaking to a bathroom mirror: "You should have told her you deliberated for weeks. Now she'll think you're shallow, you fool."

Amusement thawed her features.

"Is she getting cold feet?" He patted his pockets. "Where are my wool socks?"

"There's the Jerry I expected." She smiled.

"Better?"

She nodded. Then, seriously, she said, "It's just that I think this much money would get in the way."

"Haven't we settled this? Do I need to consult my invisible mentor again?"

"It might put pressures on us that prevent us from developing our relationship honestly. Listen, Jerry, I'm serious. If anything ever changed, if we went on the rocks and you stayed anyway. If that happened, I'd never know for sure if it was for me, or because everything you worked a lifetime for was tied up with us."

Dammit, she wanted the distance, and it bothered him. He quipped, "You could always give the money back during our first fight."

"Oh, Jerry." Sue Ann tucked the check into his inside pocket. She stayed close to him, and smiled a tilted, quiet smile. "It's late. I'd better get going."

He slid his arms around her. She came easily, naturally against him. Her breathing was faster than he'd guessed it would be; maybe she was just the smallest bit aroused, too. Her waist felt taut and slim, her hips inviting in the way they seemed to fit his. He thought of the bed a few feet away. But he reminded himself that he was going to be the one who would make her want him. That would take time . . . and self-control. He loosened the embrace.

"Jerry," she said softly. A scent like alpine meadows drifted to him. Raising up, she brushed his lips in a kiss that made him tighten his arms again, and then she whispered, "We'll play in the snow tomorrow, all right? I've got a long drive to the cabin. I should go."

Without waiting even a heartbeat, Sue Ann slipped out of his arms and walked to the door. She gave him that gentle smile. "No matter what happens, I'll always know you were willing to risk everything on us," she said, and went out.

He swore softly. What the devil did she mean, 'no matter what happens'?

As Jerry pulled off his coat, he went over the times in the past two hours that she'd drawn back from him. At the airport, she'd turned away when he'd said he was looking forward to life here. In this room, when she'd been saying how important his being here was to her, she'd walked to the window and gazed off into the snowstorm, talking not to him but to herself. Anyway, what working woman embarking on marriage would turn down a quarter of a million dollars in seed money? No woman he'd ever met, that was for sure. Was she being straight with him? Was he just too tired to look on the bright side, or had he uprooted his life to come to a woman who was having second thoughts about him?

For the first time in ten months, he doubted the wisdom of his actions.

Chapter Three

"Morning, angel."

Sue Ann burrowed completely under the quilt, bringing the telephone receiver with her. "Jerry, is that you?" she croaked, her voice roughened by sleep.

"I hope it's me," he said, sounding cheerful.

"Don't you know?"

"Well, something's missing."

"Oh, no. Your luggage didn't arrive? I'll call them—"

"Not that," he interrupted. "My stuff arrived last night."

"What time is it, anyway?" She peeped out from under the blankets and squinted at the digital clock radio. "Jerry Teal," she admonished. "It's six o'clock. It isn't even light yet."

"Wouldn't have waked you this early for the world," he said, "but like I said. Something's missing."

"What? Someone broke into your room?"

"No, angel. How can we begin our lives together when only half of us is here?"

The point of his call struck her as romantic. Snuggling down into the dark warm bed, Sue Ann murmured, "You miss me. I love hearing that first thing in the morning."

"That's only starters. After seeing you last night, holding you, I found myself up and shaving by five-thirty. If you'd been here, I might have skipped the shave and gotten right to the gourmet feast."

She sighed. "You could make a woman willingly wanton, Jerry."

"It's what I live for," he said with pretended sarcasm, quoting from a well-known movie.

"I swear," she said in a wistful tone, "you looked so handsome last night."

A pause. Then, sounding serious, he said, "About last night, Sue Ann. Occasionally I got the impression you'd changed your mind, wanted to cancel our plans."

"Referring to my moods?"

"That's all it was? Moods?"

Pushing her hair back, she wriggled up against the cherry-wood headboard. "Well, to be honest, more than a mood. We're changing our whole lives for each other," she said, hugging the covers to her chin. "We've tried to eliminate anything that would get in the way of our happiness, but you said last night we didn't know each other's inner secrets—drives, I mean. I've planned and planned, but I can't rid myself of the 'what ifs.' I'm scared, Jerry. Aren't you?"

The line crackled. In that long pause, she wondered if she'd let him down somehow. But then his voice came back warm and steady, dismissing her doubts.

"Only when you go away from me," he said. "If we can just keep looking at each other, babe. Just keep in touch. I may have come on a little strong last night, but I only wanted you to know how much our happiness means to me."

Sue Ann wanted to ask if there were other motives for handing her a quarter-million dollars, wanted to explain that she felt he was trying to manipulate her. Pray God he wasn't, but until she received the inheritance and could match more of his funds with her own—and until she was certain he hadn't misjudged her for her secrecy—she would hold back a little. None of these topics was pleasant. They would have to be explored, and soon, but not this morning. The early morning was a time for setting off on happy feet to see what the world had to offer. So, in response to his comment about how much their happiness meant to him, she said simply, "I understand."

"Okay. And one thing more before you tear out of that bed and come rushing down here to rescue this lonesome other half."

She smiled. "What's that?"

"If you hurry, there might be a surprise for you here."

She giggled. "I thought you weren't going to rush things."

"Naughty, naughty. I wasn't speaking of that. Although if you prefer to skip the snow today..."

"Incorrigible playboy. We can't skip the snow. I've got something of a surprise to share with you, too. What's yours?"

"Come and get it."

"Best offer I've had all day."

"How soon, Sue Ann?"

"An hour?"

"Make it forty-five minutes and it'll be two presents waiting for you. Plus me."

"Done. See you in forty-five. Bye—oh, and Jerry?"

"Yes, babe?"

"Thanks for waking me up. I loved it."

"Get used to it."

"I can't wait."

Chuckling intimately, she hung up.

WITH HIS PHONE CALL and the memory of being in Jerry's arms last night, Sue Ann met the crystalline morning with resolve: she would show him the bear scars today.

En route to the Breakwater, driving a little fast because she was eager to see him, she held counsel on the matter.

The chemistry between them foreshadowed passion, and not necessarily as far into the future as their wedding night. She couldn't believe how she wanted him. The admiration in his first look at her, his sure and hungry embrace, the way his lips had softened instantly when she'd kissed him, his confident warmth this morning...each detail warmed her again now. Would her scars dull that marvelous attraction?

Only once before had she cared a great deal what a man thought about the rivulets of scar tissue running down her right forearm. Mark...a hated name, even after ten years. Abruptly Sue Ann swerved away from the memories of that humiliating affair—she refused to taint the lovely morning and her prospects with Jerry.

As a rule, Sue Ann saved herself the irritation of explaining the reason for the deep gouges on her arm. At the office and at conferences, she wore suits or long-sleeved dresses. At the cabin—well, what did the crows and the salmonberries care for her scars?

She would make the revelation to Jerry as gently as possible, she decided, feeling her stomach grab at the uncertainty of his reaction.

But more than insecurity over the scars had urged her to forego that tempting bed last night, she added honestly. Some of the things he'd said had worried her. With some basic differences—questions, at least—standing between them, she would not have been able to make love with abandon, and their first time should be an act of total giving.

From the start, he talked of freedom and having a good time. Then, that business of the check—

Suddenly Sue Ann punched the brake pedal. The car barely missed contact with the bumper of a van, and Sue Ann drew in a steadying breath.

Bear scars, bad love affairs, passion. What the heck was wrong with her this morning, speeding around on dangerous roads, her mind spinning off on tangents she usually avoided?

Downshifting to ease around a pair of VWs parked up against the snowbank, she crept past a market and a gas station on the outskirts of Juneau. She'd been thinking about Jerry so constantly for so many months that to have him here within driving distance threw her whole system out of whack. Disgusted at having nearly killed herself or someone else, she issued strict orders to take her mind off Jerry for five minutes.

She'd been too absorbed to notice the grandeur of the alpine view. Now she made a point of it.

The massiveness of the mountains behind the city still amazed Sue Ann after eighteen years. To her left, Mt. Juneau seemed to thunder down on top of her. The steep slopes reached down like the hand of God from the cumulus clouds, offering rain, wind and snow, avalanche, game, the spice of evergreen, power and power outages. As a consequence, the mountains commanded with unpredictable omnipotence the lives of those who dwelled in the foothills.

Sue Ann shivered and looked away, searching for a counterpoint to the wilderness.

Ahead, to her right, the blue metal bridge spanned Gastineau Channel. It, too, was iced with white. She liked the bridge, liked the crisp authority of metal cleaving the forces of nature. Architects, steel-fitters, and the plumb lines of surveyors like Eric had joined two rugged habitats across a serpent's run, and she admired the accomplishment.

She wondered if Jerry had enjoyed the view from his room. He hadn't mentioned it when he'd called this morning.

As she braked for a traffic light, she frowned, her thoughts drifting again to her future husband. That business of the check....

In a sense, his gesture had touched her. It meant that, on the surface of things, he was trying to commit to the relationship.

But was the money supposed to be his main contribution to their relationship? she thought uneasily. Did he expect a mother instead of a wife? Someone to take care of him while he smiled at the world and told jokes and had a good time? He'd said he wanted to share it all with her, and Lord, that was what she wanted, too. She was tired of going it alone. Life in Alaska was hard. In a partnership, as she looked on their pending marriage, each had to pull his own weight while lending support to the other. It would be a tricky balance.

She wondered what he was like in a crisis.

On the other hand, she might be being unfair. After all, she was keeping a few secrets from him. The inheritance. Her insecurities. Could she let go of enough of her fears to make him happy? Could she laugh with him when he needed release? And the most difficult question—could she give her heart to him?

A car beeped behind her, and her doubts sped away as she accelerated toward the driveway of the Breakwater.

IF SHE'D NEARLY killed herself to get here, it was worth it, Sue Ann thought when Jerry opened the door. Sidelighted from the picture window, his face looked lean and smooth except for the grooves in his cheeks and the crow's-feet near his eyes, which lent him ruggedness. A lightning bolt of white and black energized the charcoal-gray ski sweater he wore, and his black jeans emphasized well-defined muscles.

As if Jerry knew how appealing he looked this morning, he grinned.

That same sudden spark of attraction she'd felt at the airport bonded them again. Eagerness lit his eyes. Desire spiraled down through Sue Ann's body.

She drew in a sharp breath and said, "Nice boots."

"You like them?" He glanced down. "An Italian miracle of weatherproofing and good leather." The grin came back like an apple popping up from underwater. "How're you?"

"Wonderful. For a while there I wondered if I was going to make it."

"Knew you would," he said, evidently thinking she was referring to the time. "Counted on it." In apparent delight, Jerry drew her into the room, kicked the door shut and pulled her into his arms. "God, I've been waiting months to be with you."

Over his shoulder she saw the mountains of Douglas Island. She'd chosen the room with exactly this moment in mind, the two of them against that backdrop, the radio playing soft music as they embraced. Closing her eyes, she relished the fulfillment.

At the confident press of his body against hers, she began to think of another fulfillment long dormant in her. His chest rose in rhythm with her breathing, like the earth coming alive to the sun. His stomach, hips and thighs fit her like a leaf sheath fits the bud, and every small movement he made to attune himself to her sent signals of virility.

"Me, too," she murmured long moments later, sliding her hands over muscles that gave his back the contours of an athlete. "I wanted this, too."

"We could always skip the field trip, hang around here," he suggested with low intimacy. "I ordered coffee, fruit, rolls."

She glanced at the table. It was set for two. "I see you did." Regretfully, Sue Ann felt a nudge of common sense. She'd wanted the business of the bear scars to be out of the way, but not here.

Turning slightly, she smiled up at him. "They'll have plowed the back roads soon. Maybe after breakfast we could take a drive out the Loop Road."

With reluctance, it seemed, he stood back from her. As he gazed at her, his gray-green eyes looked smoky. A thrill darted down her back—and a fear: how would he react to her scars? He put a gentle hand at her temple, traced it. "It's important to you, this drive?"

She nodded.

He smiled, a mischievous smile. "It's not just a ploy to divert me?"

She laughed, shook her head. "You're assuming you're the only one who likes the intimacy this room suggests. Don't ever assume that, Jerry. Alaskan women are as red-blooded as they come. But we've got plenty of time to unravel all our secrets, don't we?"

A gaze as personal as a caress slid over her red-and-black checked shirt, the red down jacket, the jeans and blue snow boots. "My hot-blooded Sourdough," he said, his eyes twinkling. "What a sight you are, with your cheeks flaming and your hair kind of wild. If they put you on the cover of *Alaska Magazine* it would start another gold rush. Juneau would be mobbed. The merchants would love you, but the legislators would threaten extradition."

Feeling young and pretty, she retorted, "They'd never throw me out."

"Oh, yes, they would."

"You mean my friends in high places couldn't save me?"

"Nope. 'Fraid not. They'd have to convene the Senate and the House by conference call because the streets would be too crowded to get to the Capitol building. The government types would be livid. The whole city would be in a panic, looking for—" He pushed a wave from her temple. "Sue Ann, you'd be a legend."

"For my blond hair? It's got gray in it!"

"No, sweetheart. For that way you have of making a man feel as if he had something important to do with his life."

Her heart beat with a strange new lightness. No man had ever filled her head with fantasies. The knowledge shocked her. What had she done with her youth, squandered her womanhood? And how, exactly, had she gotten lucky now? She gazed up at Jerry as a child looks at the ice-cream man.

He saw the look. Circling her waist, he nuzzled her ear and growled, "I'd steal you from their clutches."

"You mean, rescue me?"

"Uh-huh. Disguise you and secret you away in the dead of night."

"Exciting."

"Yes, but where?" He looked about. "Where would my Sourdough be safe?"

"My cabin," she answered, pecking him on the cheek.

"The cabin it is, then. What are we waiting for? The mob'll be here any minute." Scooping her up, he swung her in circles, as no man had ever done, and she let her head fall back, laughing with him as they spun around. "Life's an adventure movie," he said. "You're the brave heroine who keeps me from death's door."

The black-and-white horror of Bill in that newspaper story flashed before her. She hadn't been able to protect him, hadn't been able to protect herself from the pain. Chilled, she twisted away. "Lord, Jerry. Anything but that."

"Hey, babe, easy. Easy." He hugged her shoulders.

"No, Alaska's more dangerous than L.A. in a lot of ways. Believe it. You've got to be on your guard."

"Relax, Sue Ann. I'm sorry. I didn't mean to remind you of what you went through in L.A."

"I know." She eased against his chest, felt the thud of his heart, and was reassured. Wrapping her arms around him, she closed her eyes. "Just be careful, will you? Promise you won't take unnecessary risks."

"Don't worry without cause, Sue Ann. I can handle myself."

A pause, a tentative smile. "Of course you can. It's ridiculous of me to be sensitive after all these years. Let's forget it. Hey, anyway, didn't you promise me a surprise?"

He glanced down at her, and there was distance in the look, as if she'd let him down. "You okay?" he asked.

"Sure."

"All right." He patted her back. "If you'll pour the coffee, I'll get the goodies."

While Sue Ann filled their cups, Jerry went to the dressing room that held one trunk and two suitcases, his surplus luggage. Unlocking the steamer, he removed a quilt. Then he braced himself and lifted out a long chest padded with rose brocade. Coming closer, Sue Ann could see that it was beautiful and very old. The ticking on top of the case had frayed. Curious, she followed as Jerry brought the container to the bed, set it down and snapped open two ornate brass hasps.

Indicating the trunk, he said, "My grandmother's."

"I thought there might be some history. It's beautiful."

"What's in there she used only for herself and my grandfather on special occasions when they were alone. My mother gave it to me years ago." He went to the table, took a sip of coffee, then glanced at her. "I never gave it to my ex-wife, Sue Ann."

"Why not?"

"I always knew she wasn't the one to have it. You get an intuition about some things."

"But you were married for twelve years."

"She never understood me." A frown crept between his dark brows, and he glanced out the window. "Some of it was my fault, as I mentioned before. She clung, and I couldn't seem to give to her. Too worried about my mom, maybe. She was sick for years. Or perhaps too busy slaying dragons in the business world."

"That's my Harrison," she said, to cut through the somber mood.

He grimaced, drank his coffee, set down the cup. He walked to the window. Staring at the mountains, he said, "Maybe she got bored. Anyway, she wasn't fulfilled. Left. Found a route driver from a San Francisco bakery, I hear, and they bought a sailboat. Sailed off into the South Pacific sunsets together. Funny, I understand her better now."

"What do you mean?"

"She wanted the closeness I now want with you. She wanted it desperately."

Aware for the first time that his memories were bitter, she came up behind him, put a tentative hand on his back. "I'm sorry you had an unhappy marriage," she said.

He slid an arm around her and eased her up beside him. They stood that way for a while, watching the traffic move along Eagan Drive.

Presently Jerry squeezed her shoulders and said in a brighter tone, "Hey, Sue Ann."

"Hey, Jerry."

"Your surprise. Let's see what it is."

Crossing to the bed, he eased her down at the side of it and went to the chest. He lifted the lid and removed an object wrapped in dusk-rose felt, unwrapped it, and placed something shiny on the flowered bedspread beside her.

A bud vase. The patina gleamed when she picked it up. A yellow and a burgundy rose on the bowl were repeated in miniature just inside the flute of the vase, and gold glaze dusted the rim and base. Turning it over, she read, "Queen's fine bone china made in England. Established 1875." She gazed at Jerry. "It's absolutely lovely. The most delicate I've ever seen."

He tried to contain a smile, but it ghosted his lips. "Here." He ducked into the chest, withdrew and unwrapped another bud vase and laid it near her. "And here." He unveiled pairs of salad and dinner plates, cups, saucers and bowls, then removed a velvet-covered tray and put before her a delicate gravy boat and other serving dishes. Last he added tiny individual salters and small round candle holders. The whole bed gleamed with china settings for two.

The emotion welled up, misting Sue Ann's eyes. She lifted the gravy boat, touching a tiny spot in the gold rim that had been chipped. She drew in a steadying breath. It amazed her that the love of a couple from the past could issue from fine bone china, but it did; she knew the joy with which Jerry's grandparents had used these pieces, and could imagine the terrible emptiness his grandmother had felt when she had put them away for the last time. "He passed on before her, didn't he?" she asked.

"Yes. When he was only sixty-two. This set hasn't been used since then."

She brushed at her eyes. "Your mom didn't use it?"

"Like me, she never had reason."

His flat tone brought her gaze up. "Your parents weren't close?"

"Mother raised me. I didn't know my father."

"Oh." A new piece of the Jerry Teal puzzle. They'd only told each other, during one of their talks, that both their parents were dead. But now wasn't the time to dig up unpleasant memories, when he'd scattered the symbols of love like pearls around her. Replacing the gravy boat, Sue Ann rose and came into his arms. She hugged him hard, felt him return the pressure, and looked into those deep-water eyes that made her feel beautiful. "You amaze me," she whispered.

"Why?"

"The depth of feeling you've put into our future. You didn't bring these heirlooms with you and give them lightly. To you they're a legacy. I'll cherish them, Jerry. I'll serve you trout amandine and turkey dinners and Chinese chicken salad in those dishes and think about how much it means to you."

"Does that mean you'll cut me some slack about all the luggage I brought?"

"Give up the one thing I can find to tease you about?" Hiding her amusement, she shook her head. "I don't know, Jerry. I've got to have something to hold over you. You're just too perfect."

"Well, maybe this will persuade you."

He let her go. Reaching into the chest, he withdrew a flat object wrapped in green cotton.

Handing her the gift, he said, "This was given to me by my mother. It's forty-five years old or so. She bought it in the South of France when she met my father. Evidently at the time he was a guerrilla of the Maquis defending the French against the Germans, so he couldn't come back to the States with her. After she left he returned to the occupied North, and they lost touch. She never met anyone else who would give this particular keepsake meaning."

"How sad," she murmured, pulling off the covering. In her hands was an eight-by-ten silver picture frame inlaid with strips of rose-patterned porcelain. The backing showed through the glass. There was no picture in it.

"It was going to be the frame for her wedding portrait," he said.

"Jerry, I don't know what to say." *Smothered,* she wanted to say. *I feel smothered.* "All these personal treasures."

"The inlay is Limoges."

She rubbed the cool china. "It's beautiful."

"My mother gave it to me seven years ago, just before she died. 'Fill it,' she told me. 'It's not work that makes you happy, it's personal relationships. Fill it with love if you can.'"

It was the first mention of love between them. She wrapped her arms around the frame, put her chin down on the silver and thought of the argument she'd had with Eric. He wanted her to marry for love. But love took your soul when someone was ripped away from you. Losing love made you feel as if you wanted to die.

Taking it slow and easy was safer. Building on other things, like physical attraction, the need for companionship and a growing admiration for someone—these were the roots of a lasting relationship. Would she grow to love Jerry? She felt she could someday. But was it fair to him to be so careful when he was being so open? She thought about the secret she must keep from him, and turned away, feeling unfaithful.

"What is it?" he asked, coming up beside her. "Don't go away from me."

"Just . . . the pressure."

"Too much too soon?"

"I guess."

"But the wedding's only two months away. We don't want to be strangers on our wedding night, do we? We'll have this legacy to build on. That's why I'm giving you these things."

"You seem to give so much." She gripped the frame, and her fingers whitened. The mention of "legacy" made her cringe inside with guilt. Things were getting too complicated. "Jerry," she said, "there are just my hopes to give you. Just . . . wanting to be with you, wanting to make a life together."

He turned her, tilted up her chin. "Whatever you wanted to show me today will be your gift."

"It's nothing like this, though. Nothing so precious."

He put a finger to her lips. "Let me decide, will you? Listen, we'll wrap up the rolls and fruit, get the kitchen to fix us a thermos of coffee, and have breakfast out on the Loop Road, how does that sound? We'll get moving, Sue Ann, and no more sad talk."

She hesitated.

He gripped her shoulders, his eyes blazing with intent. "For the first time in my life I'm going after real happiness, Sue Ann. And nothing, not even your fears, will stand in the way."

It was a selfish, macho thing to say, but he'd said it with so much feeling it had sounded like poetry. Something inside her responded—not to the desperation his words implied, but to the possessive longing in his tone. She touched his arm. "You could write songs, Jerry. Move the multitudes with your words."

He swallowed, looked away, evidently attempting to cool his emotions. Then he said wryly, "Told you I'd make a good song-and-dance man."

She smiled ruefully.

He gave her a quick kiss on the mouth. "We'll put these things away later," he said, taking the frame, walking to the chest and laying it inside. "Right now, the first order of business is to call room service."

Relieved to be getting outdoors where she could breathe and think clearly, Sue Ann ordered the refreshments and turned off the radio while Jerry changed into pack boots that laced up to his calves. He took a black down jacket with him. With their picnic packed into a grocery bag, they climbed into the Subaru and headed out.

Half an hour later, they left the main road and drove into a wooded area, passing homes and churches tucked among the trees. Around a bend, Jerry caught a glimpse of a mass of blue ice pouring down between the shoulders of two bluffs. "A glacier," he said, his eyes lit with pleasure. "What's it called?"

"That's the Mendenhall. It flows forward about three feet a year, but melting at the face causes a net retreat of about fifty feet each year. If it had been a clear day when you arrived, you'd have seen the Mendenhall on the approach to the airport. Spectacular, isn't it?"

"It really is. Is this your surprise?"

"No," she laughed. "Not even remotely. Anyway, what I have to show you isn't exactly a surprise. Don't get your hopes up too high."

"Too late," he pronounced, reaching over to caress her hair. "I've never been more hopeful in my life."

"I'm not going to pull a rabbit out of my hat, you know. There aren't any family heirlooms buried in the snow out here."

"I bet there are. You probably don't realize they're there."

"Optimist."

"Yeah," he said, and turned toward the wilderness. His gaze roamed through the trees, as if the woods harbored secrets about her.

Ten minutes later they crossed between the huge twin logs that formed the rails of the Montana Creek Bridge. Sue Ann pulled off the road, killed the engine and climbed out. Half a dozen feet below the bridge, the stream rushed deep and fast through a funnel of concrete and rock, filling the morning with a sound like one continuous breaker hitting the beach.

Jerry walked around, stretching his arms. "Smell the air. There's nothing in it but evergreen. Unbelievable."

"Wait till spring. You'll smell moss and the new growth on the trees. And in the summer—" But she didn't tell him about the stench of rotting, spawned-out salmon. That memory she kept to herself.

Rounding the car, she popped open the hatchback, reached for her Winchester 30-06. Straightening up, she glanced around. The chill of her memories tried to crawl up her back, but she shook off the feeling.

They bundled into jackets and picked up the gear. It took them fifteen minutes to find a rock wide and flat enough for a picnic. They found the perfect place inside the first bend of the creek. Sweeping off the snow, they covered the stone with a canvas tarp and set out the food. Sue Ann propped the rifle behind her.

She'd brought apples and sandwiches from the Breakwater. Their appetites sharpened by the exercise of wading through snow drifts and scouting a location, they feasted, then lay back in the sun, holding hands.

Discussing the wedding eased the tension of waiting for the right moment to show him the scars.

Jerry's former partner, Clint Moss, would be his best man. Laura would be matron of honor, Tana the flower girl, but who would give Sue Ann away? She outlined her argument with Eric. Jerry listened, then reassured her that when the three of them felt more comfortable together, he was certain the problem would be resolved. If not, Clint would get a kick out of serving a dual role in the ceremonies.

Although she didn't mention that she'd ordered him an expensive ring as a wedding gift, she did tell Jerry that a friend from Phoenix who owned a gem brokerage would be coming up a few days early to go hunting.

When they'd exhausted that topic, Jerry once again gazed at the landscape. "This is what I wanted," he said. "I used to lie in bed at night and imagine us enjoying the wilderness and being close, talking about our lives. Such a simple thing. People don't do it enough."

She was about to murmur agreement when something caught her attention across Montana Creek.

The sun glared across fifty yards of water that tumbled around boulders and glassed over the submerged end of a huge moss-quilted log. Snow formed a finger of frosting along the trunk. Clumps of snow on the rocks caught the sun and threw white light into her eyes. She narrowed her gaze, trying to pierce the shadows on the opposite bank.

Abruptly, Jerry sat up. "Bear," he said, his voice soft and hoarse. "On the other side, near that big gray rock about twenty-five yards upstream. From my lips to your ear, Sue Ann, it's a grizzly bear."

Sue Ann reached for the Winchester, her heart somersaulting. She brought it to the ready and squinted across the water. Then she saw the hulking shoulders, the shaggy fur glistening with moisture. Hackles rose along her nape. A blond splotch on the rear hip of the bear looked familiar. "Patch," she breathed, beginning to tremble.

"Who the hell is Patch?"

"Old friend of mine."

There was silence, while Jerry's gaze shifted from one of her arms to the other. He didn't know which had the scars. "You mean . . . ?"

"Yes. Jerry, get moving, as quietly and quickly as you can. When you see your way clear to the road, start shouting. Yell your head off."

Sue Ann got to her feet. She looked down, and her chest tightened in fresh panic. Jerry hadn't moved.

"Jerry," she whispered, nudging him.

Startled, he glanced up. His face was bleached, his mouth a grim line. "I hear you," he said belatedly, and rose.

The bear hadn't seen them. With his front legs sunk in the shallows, he was drinking. Sue Ann snugged the rifle to her shoulder, took aim. She sighted on his forehead and thought, *This time we're equal.* Closer to equal, she amended. The skull of a bear was almost bulletproof, and she had only the 30-06. She lowered the sight to just behind his left shoulder, a better mark.

Jerry still hadn't moved. She felt him brush against her sleeve. What the devil was wrong with him, she wondered. "Take off, Jerry," she ordered in a harsh undertone. "I'll be right behind you."

"Yo," he murmured. She heard a muffled thump as he climbed down from the rock and slid against another. He grunted. His footsteps crunched into the distance. Feeling a rush of panic, she threw the bolt.

Through the scope she watched the grizzly jerk back, then swing around to face her. *Dear God, don't let him charge,* she prayed. The main channel ran deep and strong below her rock perch. The current would slow him, but perhaps only by seconds. He'd spent nineteen years along this water. He knew how to get around.

Patch gathered himself and leaped toward her onto a two-foot-wide rock. Sue Ann clenched her teeth. She feathered the trigger. Balanced perfectly, her old adversary rose on his haunches. The water streamed from him, glistening in the sunlight, and even as terror choked Sue Ann's breath, she admired him. On the downside of his life, he was still magnificent.

The fur on his cheeks ruffled in the breeze. Patch opened his jaws, and yellow canines gleamed. Putting herself back in time to the moment when she'd been inches from those teeth, Sue Ann felt her chest tighten. She could see his black upper jowl flapping as he mouthed her scent. His eyesight was poor, as was true of even young bears, and he turned his head from side to side, trying to gather clues that would help him decide if he were being threatened. She, too, was deciding.

Suddenly his chest pumped two or three times, and Sue Ann
knew, though she couldn't hear over the creek, that he'd made
gruffing sounds. His round ears pricked forward. Slowly he
swung his head, tracking Jerry.

The knowledge shocked her into action. Aiming for the
water curling below the bear, Sue Ann fired. The animal threw
himself backward off the rock and galloped a few yards upstream.

Sue Ann leaped off her own perch and scrambled after
Jerry. The tabletop hid the bear from view, and now the terror of not knowing what he would do pumped adrenaline into
her bloodstream. She clawed at the undergrowth, splashed into
the shallows, stumbling, wheezing in fear.

Twenty feet ahead, Jerry stood on high ground, craning toward the bear, his eyes wild. *Yell, dammit,* Sue Ann thought.
Yell.

Suddenly Jerry let out a war whoop. He waved his arms and
shouted again, following Sue Ann's progress, she guessed
from the corner of his eye.

She came puffing up to him, and they took off together,
leaping from rock to rock and crashing through brush that
dusted them with snow. Finally they reached the bridge. Running up to the log railing, panting, they scouted the stream.

Patch was lunging through deeper water, angling toward the
bank where they'd picnicked. He heaved up onto a crag of
stone and glanced into the rapids in front of him. He would
probably not chance it, she thought. The flood strength of the
current would tax him.

"Keys," said Jerry.

She pulled them from her jacket, slapped them into his
palm.

He ran to the car, jerked open the driver's door, slid in and
fired the engine. After a quick look over his shoulder toward
Sue Ann, he pulled up out of the parking spot and backed the
car onto the bridge. He sounded the horn. She jumped.

Surprised by the metallic sound, Patch lost his footing and
slid sideways into the white water. He went under.

"Jerry," Sue Ann screamed, motioning.

A memory of this bear as a yearling, bawling and clawing at
a lard tin stuck on his head, brought protectiveness flashing

through her. After the terrible price she'd paid to save Patch, and after the years he'd survived on his own, to die now, in front of her... She set down the gun and clutched the railing, searching for him. Like a breaching humpback whale, he rolled up, his back glistening, and rolled under again.

Jerry crunched up behind her. "Where is he?"

"In the water. Oh, God, Jerry, I don't want him to drown."

"There!" Jerry pointed, and Sue Ann saw the bear's head come up. His paws thrashing, he sailed under the bridge, fighting the deepest, swiftest part of the current.

Jerry and Sue Ann rushed to the other side. Downstream about thirty yards, Patch slammed into a rock. He seemed stunned, began to slide under. His mighty forearms grappled with the rock, gained purchase, slipped, and finally hooked on.

"Hang on, Patch," Sue Ann whispered. Jerry's arm came around her.

Panting out steamy breaths, hugging the rock, the bear shook his head. A silver fountain sprayed into the air and settled down. At last he got his bearings and craned toward the bridge. It felt to Sue Ann as if his eyes locked with hers. Just a split second. The feral wilderness beast in him was still there, still willing to kill. Knowing she was safe, Sue Ann could afford to grin, and she did so.

The bear blinked, rolled his open mouth in a circular pattern, and turned away.

Gathering himself, he hauled up onto the rock. Leaping from one to another, he landed on the bank and stalked into the brush. It seemed that he took his dignity with him.

Sue Ann and Jerry glanced at each other. She laughed nervously. "Let's get out of here."

Crossing the road, they picked up the rifle and piled into the car, Jerry taking the driver's seat. They rolled up the windows, locked the doors. He was shifting into first, his hands unsteady, when he swiveled and said, "Give me a little warning next time."

"I think the straight line is mine. What should I warn you about?"

"Your surprises. I'll wear my combat gear."

"He was supposed to be hibernating," she said. "He always does after it snows."

"You mean you've met up with him before? After your run-in?"

"About five years ago. Serena and I were fishing at the bridge, and he was fishing near that rock where we had our brunch. This is his home."

He shook his head in amazement. "Just like that, on my second day in Alaska, we run into a bear. *The* bear." His gray eyes shone with a mixture of excitement, fascination and fear. "You aced me, Sourdough. Your surprise topped mine. You've got heirlooms I can't believe tucked into these woods."

The timing was perfect, she thought. She would bring back the memories, and he would understand the terror she had felt when Patch's claws had ripped into her flesh. But not here. This place vibrated with challenge and terror. And not at her cabin. She wasn't ready to reveal that part of herself yet, that place of refuge where she would know whether they could be happy together.

"Jerry," she said gently, making him look at her. "We need to go someplace quiet and talk."

For a moment his gaze darted around the car, giving her the idea he felt panic. It made her heart skitter. Perhaps she should wait to show him the scars? Let the relationship ripen into a more solid friendship?

At that moment, Jerry seemed to collect his self-control. He looked at her. "Talk? What about?"

"I want to show you my scars."

Chapter Four

Jerry's insides still jumped with the aftereffects of fear. And guilt.

What if she'd been mauled again because he'd been too petrified to protect her? He'd thought for a minute Sue Ann had wanted to talk about his strange reaction to the bear, his freezing up with fear, and that had given him a jolt. But it had only been her scars. Fighting the wheel as the station wagon slid on sheets of ice buried beneath the snowdrifts, he tried to beat down the memory of his terror.

He'd sat there on the rock, staring at a grizzly that looked powerful enough to pull down a house, aware a woman was beside him—aware that he should know what to do to protect her—and unable to move. His veins had felt as if they were rigid with ice.

The crazy thing was, all he could think of at the time was Joanie, his ex-wife. Her clinging, smothering personality. A warm, beautiful woman, Joanie had been emotionally very needy. She had lived for Jerry, had waited for his attention, had had nothing going in her life but him. And in the beginning, perhaps because Joanie had reminded him of his mother, who had always needed him, he had loved her. But the attraction had died in a year, and he'd sought refuge from her accusing brown eyes and her demands on him by burying himself in ten- and twelve-hour days among the account books of his clients—people who had only needed his financial advice. He'd never understood how a sex goddess like Joanie could turn him off so completely in the bedroom, but that was how it had been. It had broken Joanie's heart, he knew, and the guilt had driven him deeper into work. *Why couldn't he have given Joanie what she needed in the marriage?* The thought had flashed into his consciousness as he'd watched that huge grizzly drink from the stream. *Would he let Sue Ann down the same way?*

He shook his head, trying to snap out of the mood.

Peering down a nave of trees that reminded him of an aisle in a cathedral he'd visited in New York several years before with his mother, he thought: *Bury the weakness. It would disgust someone as strong as Sue Ann.*

He glanced at the profile of his future wife—his future source of strength. The waves of golden hair swung with the motion of the car, giving him glimpses of a clean-lined jaw, a smooth high cheekbone and a sensuous mouth. What a woman she was. There had to be a way he could eventually be worthy of her.

Clearing his throat, he said, "You were really something back there."

She glanced at him, gave him a tense smile. "Thanks. My hands were shaking so badly I probably couldn't have hit him if he'd charged."

"I'm glad you didn't have to try to kill him."

"Me, too. Anyway, I'd have needed a cannon to stop him. A 30-06 isn't exactly a bear gun. Not in the hands of an amateur."

He drove, mulling over her comments. "Amateur." All the more reason he should've grabbed the gun. Perhaps she hadn't noticed his inaction. For now, he'd let it go. Next time he wouldn't let her down.

In a voice as quiet as a worshiper's at mass, Sue Ann directed him along the roads until they reached an open part of the wilderness, where she asked him to park. "It's through the woods," she said, climbing out, zipping her down jacket.

Jerry followed her through snowdrifts that left a residue of white above his knees. They ducked in under the trees, wound along a faint path, and came out at the side of a cabin whose stone walls and peaked wooden roof might have been constructed by giants.

Sprigs of bushes poked through the blanket of snow hugging the fieldstone wall. Under a dark and moldering eave, moss grew in clumps. A spooky aura pervaded the place, and he thought again about the grizzly.

Hurrying ahead of him, Sue Ann disappeared around the front.

He rounded a porch constructed of huge split logs, and Sue Ann cleared the stone steps two at a time. She went inside, as if she wanted a moment alone to gather her thoughts. He could hear her boots thudding across a plank floor. Maybe it *was* the scars. Women were sensitive about cosmetic beauty. Giving her time to compose herself, he looked around—and found himself in a wonderland straight out of a first-rate documentary film.

To his left, framed by overhanging branches, a lake spread out into the distance and ran into the face of the ice-blue Mendenhall Glacier. Offshore about twenty yards, an iceberg fifteen feet high floated by. On the far side of the cabin, a clump of snow fell, the branches rebounding, swishing like the wings of a big bird. The sun did not reach through the trees to lift the shadows, and the silence was eerie.

"God," he said, the cabin wall amplifying his voice as if he were preaching from a pulpit. "This place is incredible."

Behind him, Sue Ann scuffed the planks with her boots. He turned. Her blond hair glowed against the darkness of an open doorway. She stood with her hands behind her, the red jacket thrown over her shoulders and the collar turned up around her face. She looked pale.

Concerned, he leaped up onto the porch and came to her. "It kills me to see you looking like you're about to cry," he said, cupping her chin, leaning to kiss her cheek. "Talk to me, Sue Ann."

She bit her lip. "It never mattered this much before," she whispered. "I've never been so scared...."

"Hey, love, nothing to be scared about. I've tried to tell you, I admire everything about you. Your honesty, your courage—" He drew both of her arms toward him, trying to get her to unbend, relax.

And suddenly the hair on his nape rose. Beneath his fingers he felt beaded ridges of scar tissue. But they weren't little lines scratched into her right arm, they were great jagged rivulets that crisscrossed wiry, deteriorated muscle. To his fingertips, the proud flesh felt like those puka-shell necklaces from Hawaii, and he was cold clear to his spine with horror.

He drew in his breath, a sharp bite of air he should have softened to save her feelings.

Had she noticed? Perhaps not. Trancelike, she lifted her arm chest-high, and he forced himself to look at the destruction she held out for his inspection.

The scars gleamed hideously in the midday light. Four ridges of flesh, like desert arroyos bleached bone-white, ran raggedly across muscles so atrophied and stringy he wondered how she had the strength to drive or heft a rifle. She must have had butchers for surgeons.

Her voice was thin with tension when she said, "Serena was asleep in the car. I was picking blueberries in the woods. I was wearing a black-and-red plaid shirt just like this one, eighteen years ago when Patch and I had that run-in." She drew an unsteady breath, and the emotion in her voice made him cringe with the memory of his needy ex-wife.

"I would have healed okay, except for the time element," said Sue Ann. "The infection. On the way back to town, I kept fainting. Loss of blood, they said. Anyway, the next morning, a forestry guy saw the station wagon tilted over in a ditch. He said Serena was asleep on the seat next to me, holding my bad hand, so of course she was a mess, too. Blood everywhere." She shuddered.

Jerry fought past a choking feeling, and found the strength to grip her shoulders. "Take it easy, Sue Ann," he soothed. "It's all right."

She stepped back, looked beseechingly at him. "I don't know how she'd gotten into the front seat, Jerry. She was only two. If she'd been with me in the woods... if there had been a mother bear around...."

His gut lurched. He stifled a groan, and could not respond to her with words. The knowledge kept twisting inside him: through his mindlessness he might have let this happen to her again.

A bird whistled and it seemed to bolster Sue Ann. She pushed the sleeve up past her elbow, and said, "Patch had a lard tin stuck on his head. He would have died. I thought I could help him.'' She clenched and unclenched her hand, redirecting Jerry's gaze.

Perhaps it was the contrast in proximity to such destruction, but her right hand was beautiful. Long slender fingers. No enamel, just a bloom of pink beneath shapely oval nails. It could have been the hand of a pianist like Klemer. Lloyd's of London would have insured it for one million on the merit of its perfection alone. As she tugged at the cuff of her sleeve, he glanced at her other hand. It was a match. Fine-boned and delicate.

He knew he must say something. Folding her chilled hands in his, he cleared his throat and said, ''You have the most beautiful hands I've ever seen.''

Her gaze was watchful.

It was such a relief to look away from her arm that a smile, feeble as it felt, curved his lips.

Relief flashed in her eyes. And then, with her unusual sensitivity, she saw through his veil of politeness. She couldn't know he felt guilt over his own inaction when the bear had challenged them—nor could he tell her about it—so she simply assumed he was sickened by her scars, and that was in part the truth. Understanding flickered like a shadow in her gaze. Fear lent her eyes a purple cast. Pulling away her hands, she looked toward the trees.

Dammit, he vowed, this time he wouldn't buckle under the strain of a woman's emotions. Sue Ann needed his understanding.

He moved to comfort her, but she straightened away.

''Until a month after my twenty-second birthday, when my husband was killed, I thought happiness didn't end.'' Her voice grated with strain. ''I used a fantastic golden ring to keep the bad things away. I believed in fairy tales, Jerry.''

''Sue Ann, it doesn't matter about the—''

''Let me tell you,'' she whispered, squeezing her eyes shut for an instant and then opening them. She crossed the porch, stepped down to the snow, walked to the shore of the lake.

He followed, regretting that he'd reacted with such shock. Coming up beside her, he took in her shaken, vulnerable features. He longed to draw her close, erase the distance, but a ring of invisible steel seemed to keep him from her.

"I felt so betrayed after—" she indicated the scars "—these."

"By whom, love?"

"My parents."

"How exactly did they let you down?"

"By hiding reality from me."

Sue Ann bent, picked up a stone and hurled it across the surface of the lake. It skipped and sank, the ringlets widening back to them.

"We had a lovely lake at home," she added, collecting a couple more pebbles and skipping them expertly across the water. "Fields, gardens, stables. And a forest where I was sure Sir Lancelot conducted his missions of gallantry."

"I thought you 'learned romance as you grew older,'" he said, echoing her quotation from Austen. "But really, you were romantic as a child, weren't you?"

"Oh, yes. I had a pretty yellow dress with lace clear to the floor, and I used to wear it and pretend to entertain the Knights of the Round Table." She glanced at him. "Sounds silly."

"Naw," he chided, trying to lighten her mood. "Look at it this way. You're revealing more of the family heirlooms."

That brought a little smile to her mouth. She lifted her shoulders, turned, walked back to the steps. Sitting down, she motioned him to her left side and leaned against him, gazing out at the lake. The trust inherent in her posture made guilt dart through him.

Then she began to talk in a subdued voice, as if she were back in the childhood fantasy: "I would set out my little blue-and-white tea service, lean out the window over my toy box and watch for them to come in to tea."

"Who?"

"The knights. They never did, naturally, and then I'd call Mother and she'd tell me what the knights were doing to keep them out so long—little snippets from *Mort d'Arthur*. Hunting in the woods. Waging battle with other soldiers on matters of principle. Defending damsels. Fighting to preserve the realm where, so I thought, my parents were nobility who'd been asked by Arthur to tend our lands and settle quarrels among the merchants in town. My father was a judge, so he fit well into the fairy tale.

"When it had rained for weeks, I used to wave this imaginary ring of gold and command the sun to shine. Never mind that the overcast was beginning to burn off the very morning I decided it should be sunny." She laughed, a hollow sound that reverberated. "Children adapt their fantasies marvelously to their surroundings."

She began to stroke his arm, absently. "Oh, yes," she said in the tone of one who remembers another in a string of examples. "My parakeet died one day, so I waved my golden ring at poor O. Henry and commanded him to fly again. Father watched me from his reading chair.

"'Not feeling well,' he said in that same gruff-soft voice Eric uses when Tana has cut her knee. 'He'll be back tomorrow, Suzie Q, you'll see.'"

"A bird with bluer feathers sang in the cage the next morning."

"I wonder what the psychologists would have to say about that ring of yours," Jerry offered gently.

"I don't know. I suppose it stood for the ability to make the world be what I wanted it to be. Good always triumphed over evil."

She paused briefly.

"That's perfectly normal," he said, finding it easier to console her now that she was gathering back her composure. "Most kids grow up with an optimism about the world."

"All the way through college, marriage, and the birth of my daughter," she said flatly, "I was a classic Pollyanna, Jerry. I believed all you had to do was be brave and you could slay the dragons that came at you. But it wasn't true."

She abruptly stood up and faced the lake. Her jacket crackled as she pulled it around herself. "When I said 'forced into prudence in her youth,' back at the hotel, I meant when I was a young woman. I was twenty-two, actually, when I realized I had no golden ring protecting me. The dragons that eventually came at me were too big. It was awful to realize I had no power. That thought has frightened me for eighteen years."

Jerry started to stand. But an odd sensation went through him, staying him. He tried to name it and finally did. Disappointment. But why? She was vulnerable now, and perhaps had been for a minute this morning when she'd said she couldn't rid herself of the "what ifs" of their future relationship. He wouldn't be building his house upon the sand, would he? He'd been so certain she was strong, strong and reliable.

What chance at a life together would they have if both of them were afraid?

The image of her striding boldly through the snowstorm at the airport filled his mind. By God, yes, he knew a survivor when he saw one. She was just overwrought about his reaction to the scars. Women were culturally conditioned to be concerned about cosmetic beauty. He'd wounded her ego, that was all. Unintentionally he'd made too much of a nasty set of scars. She'd survived the mauling, hadn't she? It proved she was tough.

Reassured, he stood up and hugged her. "Hey," he said.

"Hey," she responded.

"Look what you've accomplished since that run of bad luck eighteen years ago."

She glanced at him. "My career? I was forced to work. I had no choice."

"You could have scrubbed floors the whole time. Instead, you went to those management classes and traveled all over trying to work your way up in the Fisheries Department. Which you did."

"I did do that, didn't I?" She smiled.

"Even today, to a lot of women, the business world is as scary as a big old grizzly. And you raised Serena, too. Another tough job. I've known women who cut all kinds of deals with guys just so they wouldn't have to face that one alone. Give yourself some credit, Sue Ann. You've slayed some monstrous dragons in your time. I admire your courage."

"Eric was there. I couldn't have done it without him."

"No, now, don't deal yourself half a hand. After all, it took guts to break with tradition and send for a swell guy like me to tuck you in at night."

She chuckled softly.

It became easier to lighten up, joke around. He took her hand, nuzzled her hair, said against her ear, "You don't fool me, you gorgeous bear-fighting businesswoman."

"Jerry," she protested.

"You're just trying to inflate my male ego, telling me the world is full of dragons that frighten you."

"You think so, huh?" Her tone was wry.

"Yep. So no more of this reverse-psychology stuff. It's wasted on me. My male ego is alive and well. I've slayed my share of dragons and I know how tough it is, and I'm here to tell you, the future Mrs. Teal, you impress the hell out of me."

"I impress you that much, huh?" Tugging his chin, she smiled. But a thought evidently worried her; her eyes clouded and the smile faded. "What if I need a strong shoulder once in a while, Jerry?"

It was a moment before he could say with conviction, "Hey, I'll be there. We'll be there for each other. That's what marriage is all about, isn't it?"

She, too, hesitated, searching his features. When he smiled encouragingly, she sighed, nodded, and snuggled into his arms.

He tightened the embrace, held her hard, rocking her. He meant it. He'd be there when she needed him. Marriage was like a going business: the checks and balances, the giving and taking on both sides, kept the relationship in the black.

What would it cost him?

He'd have to bury his insecurities, submerge that gnawing need for unfettered freedom. To find the will to do that, he'd remember the trade-off—the loneliness of single life. For strength, he'd call upon his own years of hard lessons. To keep hope alive, he'd borrow Sue Ann's mythical golden ring if he had to. He'd do anything, everything within his power to make their lives happy.

The fear of failure tried to shove its ugly head into the plans he made. But as a businessman he was used to facing the threat of failure. He held on to that nub of experience. Yes, he told himself—harshly, to make it stick—it was possible to find happiness with Sue Ann. Just look at the raw material he had to work with.

He ran his hands over her shoulders, feeling the wiry strength of her melt slowly as his caresses grew gentle. Strong but feminine, he thought. An incredible combination. He was lucky. She was so lovely. The scars didn't matter at all.

He let her go. Drawing her right arm to him, he bent down and gently kissed the marks of the grizzly bear.

SEVEN OF THE BEST DAYS in Sue Ann's lifetime passed with the same closeness, laughter and mental challenge she'd shared with Jerry at Montana Creek and Skater's Cabin. As the days unfolded, she was very clear that she had purposely allowed peace of mind to reign over their lives.

She had pushed back her fears about the marriage, and hadn't pressed him for explanations about the check, for example, because she refused to mar the beauty of getting to know his good side.

Nor did they make love. At Skater's Cabin, he had kissed her scars, accepting them. At dinner the next night at the Baranoff Hotel, she'd worn a burgundy wool dress with long, billowing sleeves. He had found the scars through all that material and had run his fingertips over them, loving and accepting. She had wanted, then, to take him home with her and make love. But the moment had passed. They had said goodnight with a longing that still lived when they saw each other the next morning. When the longing built and they clung to each other, he kissed her with a creative genius that left her shaking. Still, he didn't pressure her to give in. He seemed as willing to wait as she.

If Sue Ann wondered at the motive for his control and consideration, she kept even that negative aspect at bay. She began to look on their happiness as a solid base from which they would build a marriage and weather later crises. And the hope mounted in her.

Sue Ann did devote a moment or two to worrying over his paralytic response to Patch; after all, the near-attack had been the first crisis they had faced together. But she told herself it was natural, even healthy, to be afraid of such ferocious strength. At least for the first time. Telling him about the sourdough knack of banging on tin cans and shouting when traveling through the woods, and about avoiding eye contact if he ever came face-to-face with a bear, she let the topic drop. The whole subject of bears wearied her.

So there was really nothing she would permit to come between them in those days of discovery. It was as if, in telling him about the golden ring, she had waved it again and watched it surround her life with perfection. How good it felt to live once more, even temporarily, in fantasyland.

In that first week, they did the things couples do in wintertime Juneau when they are between commitments and free to follow their own itineraries. They laughed with delight when a child pandered an Eskimo ulu so earnestly they felt compelled to buy the skinning knife; they ate steaming, deep-fried fish sticks at a kiosk outside the classical Greek columns and marble steps of the Capitol building; they drank beer and scuffed around in the sawdust in the Red Dog Saloon; to satisfy Jerry's curiosity, they drove over the sixty-odd miles of road connecting Juneau with the outback; and they walked along the tidal shores of North Douglas, barely aware of the calls of sea gulls and seals offshore or the creatures of the rain forest at their backs, because they were attuned to one song— their own.

But eventually, Sue Ann sensed that Jerry wanted a wider social life. After seeing his restlessness when visiting the florist to order flowers for the wedding or meeting the minister, Sue Ann realized she was better suited to the preparations than he. And on a number of occasions he'd asked about Eric. "What does he do in the evenings?" he'd say. "What do Eric and his friends do for entertainment after work?"

Even as the golden ring began to lose its firm outer edge, she couldn't blame Jerry for needing more scope in his life. Migrating from a teeming city and a busy social life to a comparative outpost, and to one woman, had to engender a form of culture shock. He was an outgoing, people-loving man. He needed a circle of friends. He needed activity centered on his outdoor interests.

Sue Ann thought she could fix the problem. First, they rented a car for Jerry. When she was busy mailing wedding invitations and running other errands, he struck out on his own. On Friday afternoon a week later, after agreeing to meet that night, she left him downtown at a sporting-goods store and returned to her cabin, where she made some phone calls.

In five minutes she'd arranged to take Jerry to a nightclub at the waterfront, where a group of her friends and Eric's would welcome him properly. She'd dropped a few heavy hints that Jerry wouldn't turn down invitations to go out with "the guys."

Telephoning Serena to share her happiness, she heard the excitement in her daughter's voice when she said she was looking forward to meeting Jerry. Serena made her famous "Go for the gusto" speech, and it brought tears to Sue Ann's eyes.

"Come up and stay with me the week before the wedding," she urged. "We can run errands together and talk for hours. We'd lunch with Jerry, and I'd get to brag about your honors grades and all those offers you're getting to join design firms. I miss you so much, sweetheart."

Serena's voice choked up. "I can't, Mama. I miss you, too, but I'll be cramming for quarterfinals until I catch my flight, and then I come back five days later to take them. You know what crushers they are. If there was any way...."

"I know, darling. At least you'll spend the night before the wedding with me. We'll catch up then, okay?"

They said an emotional goodbye, and Sue Ann sat by her telephone for long minutes, missing the contact with someone so close to her, wanting Serena's confidence to stay with her through the weeks ahead.

Talking to Serena had reminded her how important family closeness was to her peace of mind.

She hadn't called Eric, of course. Having decided she and Jerry needed time alone to get to know each other, she hadn't sought him out since the fight. Nor had he left any messages on her telephone recorder. Eric had never held a grudge so long.

The distance between them saddened her. She missed his chaffing good humor. She missed the warmth and love of his family. She missed his approval. His silence was the one thing out of place in her life, and she worried about patching things up.

So while she bathed and put on a blue sweater dress this Friday evening, she made a new resolution. As soon as Jerry accepted an offer to get out with the boys, she would find Eric, tell him how happy she was, and ask him to forgive her for

planning her marriage without him. She would mend the rift.
She would bring her brother back into her life.

Lulled by her own happiness, she couldn't begin to imagine
what price Eric would exact as retribution for his isolation.
She'd never hurt him this badly before.

Chapter Five

Ushered in ahead of Jerry, Sue Ann peered through the smoke and dim light of the cocktail lounge, trying to spot her colleagues from the office. The scents of oregano and pepperoni wafted to her on waves of body heat. A yeasty aroma mingled with the grass-fire smell of burning cigarettes. She side-stepped a couple of bear-sized fishermen in cotton shirts, jeans and rubber boots. In fact—the image was familiar—the oblong room seemed filled with bears with bushy beards and broad shoulders, and the bubble and roar of voices reminded her of the rush of a stream where bears might feed.

The door slammed, and Jerry came in from parking the car. Glad she had backup in the chaos, Sue Ann took his arm. The dark jeans, blue-and-black plaid shirt and black down jacket set off his tan and his gunmetal-gray-and-black hair. While his clothes still bore the sheen of an expensive clothier, they were simple and would put her friends at ease, she noted with pride. He knew how to fit in.

Jerry took in the sights: the dory suspended overhead by chains, the rusty gold miners' pans nailed to pine studs, the musket racked in elkhorns above the long bar. The smile of a man coming into his element slanted across his face. He scanned the narrow picture windows that framed the patrons: like gulls on a fence, the crowd clung to a wide window ledge, silhouetted against lights outside that reflected off ice-glazed pilings and the slippery gleam of Gastineau Channel. Jerry appeared to inventory the blinking, beeping video games along the east wall. His gaze panned the long bar, jammed with men and women who laughed and drank from beer glasses. At last he heaved a sigh of satisfaction.

"This place must drag in a fortune," he said, the respect unmistakable. "Wonder who does their financials."

"Thought you were retired," she said.

"Yeah." He shot her an appreciative glance. "Yeah, you bet I am. It's time to party."

She felt a tug inside. There was a tad too much in his tone that suggested he'd been cooped up. But he had, hadn't he, she argued. And she'd arranged this night to widen his social circle.

His head sweeping like a surveillance camera, Jerry nudged her forward through the crowd, heading for the bar. Someone touched Sue Ann's coat sleeve. She hung back to see who it was.

"Sue Ann, don't you look terrific," said a smooth-shaven man of thirty-six whom Sue Ann recognized as the Assistant State Attorney General. "Blue becomes you."

"Bob," she said in delight. "It's been months. How are you?"

"Great. Down for the fall session, running interference for the boss, keeping busy."

"All those dues you're paying, Bob. Carl had better keep his bench skills honed."

Bob laughed, evidently pleased at the innuendo he might someday take over the prestigious state office. His gaze flickered with interest over Jerry, at her elbow.

"Jerry," she said, turning to curve her arm through his. "Meet Bob Bradley with the Attorney General's office. Bob, this is Jerry Teal, late of Teal & Moss Financial Services in Los Angeles."

"Late?" said the lawyer, shaking hands.

"Retired," said Jerry.

"Engaged." Sue Ann smiled. "I sent the reception invitation to your office. I hope you and Carl won't be too tied up to stop by Mike's Place for a glass of champagne."

"Short of a major setback on the water issue, nothing could keep me away," he said, ever the diplomat with the charming grin. "I'm sure I speak for the Attorney General as well. You realize, of course, you're breaking half the hearts in the House and Senate, Sue Ann. Marrying a money man from our arch-rival in tourism, California.'' His gaze scanned the couple. "Are we losing a daughter or gaining a son, euphemistically speaking?''

"'Alaska or bust,' I believe is the phrase,'' said Jerry. "Afraid I've risked it all for your fair state and its bounty.''

The two men glanced at Sue Ann and chuckled, and she felt pleased to have accomplished so much—letting the bureaucrats have a look at Jerry—in so short a time. Jerry had handled the moment with grace.

The attorney yielded the game with a nod of approval. "Can't fault your taste, Jerry. Look forward to seeing you in a few weeks.''

He moved away.

Jerry ran his hand over Sue Ann's back, the gesture decidedly warm. "You *do* have friends in high places. But I get the impression it's not the House and Senate hearts that are broken over our engagement.''

"Don't be silly, sweetheart. I never encouraged him. I don't date his type. Not since—'' The old hurt, the humiliation of loving Mark flashed over her, and she plunged to a stop.

"Since when?'' prompted Jerry.

Sue Ann told herself to buck up, that she needed her wits about her at Jerry's coming-out party. "Since I had to work with the government types on a professional basis. I'm one of those women who are sensitive about conflicts of interest.'' She forced a smile. "I've got a thirst as big as a mountain, how about you?''

"You bet. Beer?''

She nodded. "I'll go look around, see if the gang's here.''

He kissed her cheek. "Don't get lost.''

"I have a feeling you wouldn't let that happen.''

The grin surfaced. "You think I'm crazy? I don't want my heart thrown on the ash heap over at the House and Senate.''

She swatted his sleeve and ducked around him, feeling pleased with herself for controlling her unpredictable emotions, feeling happy with Jerry for being so adaptable in new situations. She was a bit of a feminist at heart—but she liked a man who valued his woman. Jerry, it seemed, was the type to show it.

How would he take it when her male friends buddied up to her?

She spotted one of them, a husky comptroller from Payroll who looked less like a financial man than a logger trying to adapt to city life. As usual, Melburn's brown tweed sport coat rode up at the wrists and bowed at the lapels. If he weren't the sharpest accountant in the world, his body balanced the assets; it was tuned like a racing engine. Seeing Sue Ann's hand raised in greeting, he abruptly stood up. His chair teetered and he spun, grabbed it, steadied it and waved her over, his movements fluid and fast.

He was with his girlfriend, Brenda, a feisty brown-haired woman who ran the mail room at Fisheries.

Sue Ann came up to the table, shrugged out of her coat and took the chair Melburn held out for her. "How's everybody?" she asked, smiling at the couple.

"Blackburn." Mel nodded in his crisp way. He sat down. "Wondered how long it would take you to come out of hibernation. Where's the dude?"

"What dude? Oh, you mean Jerry. He's no dude, Mel."

"Remains to be seen. Where is he?"

"Getting the beers."

"You get hitched yet?"

She rolled her eyes. "You know very well the wedding's not for weeks. You know because you're going to be there."

"I like a pushy woman." He took a swig of beer. "Your brother doesn't like it much, but then Eric has this fragile ego. Always in need of replastering, if you know what I mean. I hear he's miffed about the dude."

Sue Ann's insides dipped. " 'Miffed' is an understatement. I haven't seen Eric, Mel. How's he doing?"

"Doing? Eric? The usual."

"What's that?"

"Snarling like a hound dog whose favorite bone got swiped. Driving us all crazy. Organizing the moose hunt as if it were a mission in Nam. I told him to cool it, it would all come together fine. No hassle. Your dude hunt?"

Mel looked intently past Sue Ann's shoulder. Sensing Jerry was approaching, Sue Ann turned, invited him over with a smile, and said offhandedly to Mel, "Ask him if he hunts. Here he is."

She took the beers from Jerry and set them down, introduced him to her friends and moved so he could pull his chair closer to the table. He hung his jacket over the bentwood back. Rolling up the cuffs of his sleeves, he sat down.

"We gotta know right off the bat, Teal," said Mel. "You a man to go out hunting?"

"You bet. Looking forward to it. I brought my gun collection up in one of my steamer trunks."

"Dig 'em out, then. Moose season's almost gone."

"Can I still get a license and tags?"

"Nope. But you ought to come on up the river anyway. Get your bearings for next year."

Satisfied that the door had been opened for Jerry, Sue Ann steered the conversation to accounting, and Mel referred to her talk with him earlier in the day. "Sue Ann tells us you were playing ball with the big boys," he said to Jerry. "Working with legal types on mergers, acquisitions, that kind of thing."

"That's right," said Jerry. "We set up Teal & Moss to be a full-service financial firm." He tugged at his ear. "Estate work, investment portfolios, Chapter Elevens, liquidations, tax consulting for the guys who have six or eight zeros behind their signature. The whole ball of wax."

"Tends to make you quick on your feet in a crisis, a background like that. Impressive." Someone near the video games caught Mel's attention, and he beckoned to them.

"Maybe," Jerry said under his breath. "But you can't see the scars." He leaned toward Sue Ann and kissed her.

And then, over his shoulder, she saw Eric coming toward the table, and she pulled back, steeling herself for what surely would be a confrontation. Eric wasn't a soft, floppy hound dog, as Mel had suggested. He was a pit bull when he was crossed.

Jerry was tall and had his back to Eric, shielding Sue Ann, so her brother's glance only took in the others. Pulling off deerskin gloves and pushing them into his pockets, he removed a wool peacoat and said, "Mel. Brenda. Colder than a snowstorm in January out there."

"Hey, bud," Mel laughed, clapping him on the back. "Thought you were confined to barracks tonight."

"I was. Then eight bunny rabbits with pigtails and high voices burrowed in." Eric grinned. "A slumber party is a good excuse to come to town."

"I hear you. Grab a tree and sit on it."

"Yeah, right." Eric craned around, spotted an empty chair and went to get it.

A waitress took Mel's order for a pitcher of beer and an extra mug. Eric came back and slid his chair between Mel and Brenda.

And then he glanced across at Sue Ann. All friendliness faded. When his gaze slid to Jerry, a curiosity and then a hardness flickered over his features.

Mel—good old Mel—cut into the silence with a hearty, "Teal, here, likes to hunt, Eric. We have us another hunting buddy. What gun'd you say you were taking up the Taku River, Teal?"

Mel had bulldozed Jerry into the hunting trip, and Eric's face darkened, but he didn't object.

Jerry paused only an instant before saying, "The Remington 700, I think. It's outfitted for the 375 H & H Mag. ammo. It should keep the bears off my back, anyway." He cast a brief glance at Sue Ann, as if to tell her he *could* handle a run-in with a bear. Then Jerry was standing, leaning across the table, his hand extended to Eric. "Sue Ann makes you out a hero. It's good to finally meet you. Jerry Teal."

The moment stretched out. The tension rang like bells on Easter Sunday. Sue Ann's heart thudded as she watched Eric ignore the hand.

"Eric, you—" she said tersely.

But at the same moment, Eric's large hand came up from the darkness and slowly gripped Jerry's. And squeezed. Hard.

Jerry's palm went white around the edges. His generous mouth thinned. Then a muscle ticked in Eric's cheek, and it was evident Jerry's grip had hardened.

Sue Ann began to rise from her chair. Through tight lips she said, "Jerry likes Alaska, Eric. So far."

"I wouldn't want to disappoint him," Eric said through gritted teeth.

Mel laughed. "Why don't we have a good old-fashioned arm wrestling? Settle the score of the ballgame. What d'you say?"

A pitcher of beer sliced down between the two men and rocked the table. "Hello. No roughhousing," the waitress announced, nudging the handclasp apart with another pitcher and a mug. "Mel, you're a troublemaker. Behave yourself."

"Yeah, Mel," Brenda said. "Behave yourself."

Mel glanced at the ceiling. "Why me, Lord? I been good."

The waitress grinned at him. "That's what you keep saying, Mel, but who believes it?" She said hi to Sue Ann, then glanced at Jerry. "New in town?"

Mel said, "This is Jerry, Sue Ann's fiancé. He's in my line."

"Nobody's in your line, Melburn," she said, hefting her tray of glasses. "You're in a class by yourself. Not even the brown bears would claim you." She offered a final smile. "Congratulations, you two. Gotta run."

Everyone was overly busy for a moment, refilling glasses and mugs with draft. Brenda lit a cigarette. Beneath the table, Jerry took Sue Ann's hand and squeezed it. Returning the caress, she met his gaze, silently expressing regret and embarrassment. He gave her a little it-doesn't-matter shrug.

Mel got up, flipped his chair around the wrong way and sat on it, propping an arm on the bentwood back. He squinted at Eric. "I heard the big one came through."

Wiping beer suds from his lips, Eric set down his mug. He grimaced with the closest thing to a smile he could probably muster, given the recent confrontation, but it was evident he was pleased. "Yeah, the contract's due in any day. I got a call from my client this morning. On the strength of his promise, I asked Seattle to ferry up the extra equipment I'll need and I lined up a helicopter and pilot. I'm running ads in the *Post-Intelligencer* and the *Empire* this weekend. I gotta round out my crews, be ready to clear brush. The time-line on this job is tight."

For Jerry's benefit, Mel canted around and said, "Eric's survey company landed a big-bucks contract to survey access to a mine on Admiralty Island."

Everyone glad-handed him, praised him. Genuinely happy for Eric, Sue Ann leaned forward and said, "That's wonderful news, Eric. I'm thrilled for you."

The lines on either side of his mouth softened. "Yeah, well," he said, lifting a shoulder, "the timing was good."

He might have meant, of course, that he'd miss the wedding. But that was between them. Or he might have been referring to financial concerns. He and Laura had had a rough time of it last winter.

It was one of those moments when timing was important. No one thought to toast Eric's accomplishment—no one but Jerry. Hefting a pitcher of beer, he topped the glasses and said, "I admire a man who takes risks in the business world." He came to Eric's mug, and when he'd filled it, their gazes held for a moment. Color flagged Eric's cheeks. He looked away in consternation. Jerry moved on, saying, "Taking risks steals your sleep, puts pressures on you nobody can see or really understand unless they've been there. When you've taken the right risk and won, you deserve to be recognized." He set the pitcher down. Raising his glass, as the others did in turn, he said clearly, "To Eric's success on the mine project."

"Eric's success," the others echoed, clinking glasses.

Had Jerry been referring to the risks he'd taken to come north, Sue Ann wondered. Every day there seemed to be a new subtlety about her fiancé, a new point of view to worry her. What was behind Jerry's jokes and his gifts and his talk of risks? She glanced at her brother, wishing she could talk to him.

Several times, Eric ducked his head in thanks, the hair over his forehead bobbing like a spruce branch. His mouth was screwed up with the effort to accept praise from a man he obviously didn't trust.

"Well," Mel pronounced. "We can hardly ignore the other risk at hand, if you'll pardon my stealing your words, Teal."

"Go right ahead," said Jerry.

"To Jerry and one of the gutsiest ladies I've ever had the dubious pleasure of tangling with in a business meeting, Blackburn herself. You'll have your hands full, Teal."

"Mel," scolded Brenda.

Sue Ann felt delight tingle through her. But it was tainted by a longing for Eric's approval. As the glasses chimed around her, she met Jerry's warm gaze, acknowledged her smiling colleagues, then sought Eric's expression. He'd raised his glass—what else could he do, under the circumstances?—but his mouth was a line of bitterness. She urged him with her eyes. "Come on," she whispered. He couldn't hear, but he understood. He looked toward her for an instant. Finally, shaking his head, he pushed his mug into the air and touched her glass. She mouthed, "Thanks," and turned away because if she held the look, her eyes would begin to mist.

AN HOUR SLIPPED BY. Brenda kissed Mel's cheek and said she had to get her beauty sleep. She left the bar. A bowl of peanuts and two new pitchers of beer were three-fourths empty, and Eric seemed almost relaxed. The men talked about the moose hunt, clinked mugs, and Sue Ann waited for a sense of relief. Instead she felt uneasy. Behind Eric's facade of friendliness, a slow burn in his eyes reminded her of a wolf watching a rabbit. What did Eric resent in Jerry? What was he waiting for?

"Before you got here tonight," Mel was saying to Eric, "I was about to ask Teal about his plans." He waved his mug at Jerry. "You think you'll hang out a shingle here in town?"

Jerry popped some peanuts into his mouth and chewed thoughtfully. "Thought I'd take some time off, Mel," he said. "L.A.'s the kind of sweatbox that drains your ambition."

"Must be nice, kicking back like that," Mel said wistfully.

"Yeah," Eric said into his mug, distorting the sound of his voice so much Sue Ann couldn't read his tone. He took a big slug of beer.

"Hell—" Mel shook his head "—you might as well enjoy life if you've got the chance. Do some fishing, hunting."

"Just what I planned to do. Enjoy life." Jerry leaned over and kissed Sue Ann.

Eric snapped his mug to the table. Sue Ann looked up, saw his bleached features, and straightened in alarm.

"Maybe you could send Sue Ann back to work," Eric said, his jaw clenched. "Keep you in cigars and champagne."

Jerry's smile froze. "If you've got a problem, McMillan," he said in a low voice, "maybe you should put your cards on the table. What are you driving at?"

"You, Teal, that's what." Eric's fists knotted. He rose, his facial muscles quivering. "You come up here in your fancy clothes and your stateside haircut, thinking you can barge in on the good life. What'd Sue Ann say you were, forty-five? And *retired*? Nobody kicks back at your age in this neck of the woods. They work their guts out to get by. No, sir, maybe you've fooled Mel, here—" he jerked his thumb at Mel, then Sue Ann "—or her, because she's desperate for a little happiness for a change, but you don't fool me."

Jerry flattened his palms on the table and pushed himself up. "You're out of line," he said. "Sure, I like to have a good time. But you're jumping to conclusions you know nothing about. Take it easy—"

"No," Eric barked. "I won't take it easy. I know where you're coming from, and I don't like it. You're here for a free ride. You expect to go hunting and fishing with me and my friends, and mooch off Sue Ann and have a good time with her because she's a damned good-looking broad for forty. But I'll tell you something." He gripped the edge of the table, bleaching his knuckles. "I'm here to make sure you pay your own way, dude."

Sue Ann's hands shook. Her face contracted in spasms, and her insides felt like the San Andreas Fault during an 8.0 shaker. She rose unsteadily.

Something snagged the sleeve of her sweater dress, and she looked down. Jerry's hand was on her arm. Still standing, he eased her back to her seat.

His jaw rigid, his eyes glittering a pale cold gray, he reached down into a pocket of his jacket and dragged out some papers. "Sue Ann is the woman I plan to spend the rest of my life with," he said in clipped words. "For her sake, to try to undo some of the pain you've caused her tonight..." He flung the check he'd tried to give her a week ago next to a round ashtray. "Go ahead, McMillan, take a good look," he said harshly. "It's the money I tried to give Sue Ann when I arrived. A kind of good-faith deposit on our future. But she wouldn't take it. Said it might harm our chances at a good marriage. I'd say it pays my way for the first year or so, wouldn't you?''

Her brother's gaze shifted to the check, registered the amount, and lifted to Jerry's face, but he didn't reply.

"Wouldn't you?" Jerry repeated.

"Hey, man," Eric began, sounding confused, sinking to his chair.

Looking away in disgust, Jerry toyed with an envelope he still held, seeming to rethink a tough decision.

Mel glanced to his left, his right, surveying the crowd; they were noisy and unaware of the argument. He gave Sue Ann a glance of sympathy, but she was so furious she couldn't acknowledge it. She riveted her attention on Jerry.

Removing a sheaf of folded white pages from the envelope, he said, "When Sue Ann refused my donation to the kitty, I thought about it. She's right, my people back in L.A. are right. Money shouldn't cloud things. I had planned to reserve this document for her eyes only, but the hell with it."

He snapped the sheets open and tossed them on the table, then sat down.

As one, Mel, Eric and Sue Ann leaned forward. The heading on the top sheet read, "In the matter of the marriage of Jerald Edward Teal and Sue Ann McMillan Blackburn, a Premarital Settlement Agreement."

In the text she glimpsed, "Each party retains monies and assets, whether earned to date or held in trust prior to the marriage..."

Her emotions had already been through a gauntlet of stresses, and now they leaped and twisted like some spring-crazed lamb in a pasture. What did the prenuptial mean—that he wanted to prove he had faith in their relationship? That he wanted Eric and everyone to know he wasn't a gold digger? Or was it that he wanted to lock her in? Yet what right had she to question his motives, she thought, with the inheritance a secret between them? Suddenly her guilt gave way to relief. If she signed the prenuptial, maybe it would ease her conscience about the secret. Yes, it was a good thing, this document. It clearly separated finances from romance.

The mixture of feelings rushed through her nervous system, jamming up in the narrow channel where tears originate, and she brushed at her eyes. She reached out, blindly, and found Jerry's hand. It was stiff with tension. She looked at him.

His jaw jutted with anger at the public airing of their private affairs. But his eyes glowed with pride and uncertainty.

They came together in an embrace. Although she normally drew back from public displays of affection, nothing mattered as much as this hug from Jerry, because it was hard and reassuring. The world could look or look away; it didn't matter.

He muttered something she couldn't quite hear. "What?" she said, holding him.

"Let's cut a trail," he said against her hair, his low voice and his warmth familiar to her, familiar and suddenly essential. She nodded yes against his chest.

Mel said something about his alarm clock being a damned nuisance in the morning. Eric grumbled a response. Jerry and Sue Ann unfolded themselves and turned around.

Eric's pitching-hand grasped the check and the papers. He held them out to Jerry, who folded them away. "I may have misjudged you," Eric said haltingly. "But I don't know how to take the idea of the check and the legal stuff. Give me a while to get used to—" his hand fluttered between Jerry and Sue Ann "—the whole thing."

"Eric, I can appreciate how you're feeling," Jerry said in an even voice. "But I'd take exception to prolonged hostility between you and me—for Sue Ann's sake."

"You can't discount the differences we have, after the years we've been close."

"Speaking of which," said Mel with uncanny timing, flinging down some bills, "it's getting close to my bedtime. The beers're on me. I can't say it's been an easy welcome, Teal. But then this is Alaska. I'll give you a call, see if you want to get in some target practice tomorrow." He turned, nodded. "Eric. Sue Ann. Try not to get along so well, will you? Makes the party dull."

He saluted, grinned, and headed for the door.

The three of them stood, shrugged into coats. Eric said something about seeing someone at the bar before he left, offered a stilted good-night and disappeared.

Sue Ann took Jerry's hand, and he bent to kiss her on the forehead. "Everything'll work out," he said, his smile indulgent.

"I don't know. We've got a long way to go before Eric gets into a tuxedo to give me away."

He snipped her nose with a finger. "Quit worrying."

"You're right. We've accomplished a lot tonight." Squaring her shoulders, she smiled. "If you're planning to go out shooting with Mel tomorrow, will you save me the evening? Dinner at my place. A real date?"

"You mean I passed muster?"

Sue Ann pulled away in surprise. It was perceptive of him to notice that she'd carefully managed each plateau they'd attained as a couple. She'd introduced him to Juneau and the surrounding country, he'd seen her scars, he'd met some of her friends and her brother, and now it was time to see the home they would share. Step by step, she'd brought him into her life. So far, it felt safe. It felt right. She wondered briefly if he resented her purposeful methods, but the warmth of his gaze reassured her.

Still, she hesitated. It made perfect sense for a man in Jerry's financial position to want to secure his assets with a prenuptial agreement. And while asking her to sign it relieved her conscience, why had he brought it up now? Why hadn't he brought up the subject months earlier, when they'd set the wedding date?

Evidently Jerry sensed why she was quiet. His brow furrowing, he took out the marital document, tapped it against his knuckles. "I know my handling of this was abrupt, the timing awkward," he said, handing it to her. "Just read it. Let me know if you want anything changed. We'll talk about it tomorrow night."

His understanding reassured her. She smiled. "Eric upset me. I'm worrying over nothing. Of course you passed muster, Jerry. You're a good man, and I'm sure you have nothing but our best interests at heart."

"Atta girl." He laid a hand against her cheek. "Just hang in there, Sue Ann. You'll prove me worthy yet."

As he ushered her toward the door, the notion persisted that he was asking for reassurance, and she wondered what was really in Jerry's heart.

Chapter Six

A dusty placard of Marilyn Monroe dominated the display window of Face, Feet and Fingers, the tiny beauty shop on Franklin Street. The black-and-white poster was unusual in that the star's hair had been tipped with orange and a lightning bolt in shades of tangerine and lavender darted across one of her eyebrows.

Sue Ann shook her head at Vivian's sense of humor and went inside.

As usual, she barely got past the softly droning TV set and the torn-up easy chair flanking the cash register before hearing one of Vivian's off-the-wall epithets.

"Tough tamaytas," Viv said to someone on the telephone. "Just tell him tough tamaytas, you won't pay the extra rent."

Then she glanced up, held an aging, elegant hand over the receiver, and said to Sue Ann, "Hi, sweetie. Be with you in a minute."

When Sue Ann nodded, she went back to her caller. "Mary, tell him when he fixes the plumbing in the bathroom, the wall heater in the hall and that rattle in your dishwasher, you'll be happy to pay another twenty-five a month."

She listened, brushing at coiffed red hair that refused to require Miss Clairol—a fact that amazed Vivian and everyone else who knew the truth, that she was nearing retirement age. Viv's molded features made you look twice, Sue Ann thought. Faceted in the latest fashion, her glasses had thick lenses that enlarged already-striking blue eyes.

When she took off her glasses, as she did now, tapping the bridge against her open appointment book, she displayed her usual good-humored impatience.

"Okay, sweetie," she said to wind up the call. "Just don't accept that date for dinner. He's playing games with you. Oldest trick in the book. Listen, Mary, I'll meet you tonight at the Baranoff for drinks and we'll go from there."

She hung up. "Put down your purse and be comfortable," she said, waving Sue Ann to a manicure table flanked by a cabinet cluttered with emery boards, bottles of nail-care products and a box with a rope of cotton trailing out of it. Sitting down, Sue Ann pushed up the sleeves of her red sweater. Her friend patted the pocket of her turquoise jumpsuit and pulled out a long nail file. Viv sat down across the narrow table from Sue Ann and took her right hand, peering critically at the healthy nails. "That was Mary Hall," she said, beginning to run the nail file along the smallest fingernail. "She's a pushover for a tough-talking man. She should have spent the years I did down in the Mojave Desert in the early days of the space program. Fending off those pilots' macho moves would have put teeth in her backbone."

Sue Ann grinned at the odd word-picture.

"Your hands are dry," Viv chided. "You're forgetting to use lotion, and they'll end up looking like lobster shells at the wedding."

"He'll know he's marrying an Alaskan."

"What kind of attitude is that?" The large blue eyes flicked over Sue Ann's face, then narrowed on the rhythmic sawing of the nail file. "Just because you live at the edge of the wilderness is no excuse to look like a pioneer. A man wants a woman who's polished. Soft and clean and shining, like good satin." She chuckled. "I don't have to tell you. You know. You keep yourself up."

"I'm glad you could work me in. Tonight I'd like to look like satin."

Viv glanced up. "What's happening tonight?"

"I've invited him to dinner. At my place."

"The big plunge, huh?" Smiling sagely, Vivian held up a nail to check the shape, then went back to buffing it. "I tell you, it does my heart good to see you marrying, Sue Ann.

We've been friends a long time, and I can speak my mind now because it doesn't matter.''

"About what?"

"I was worried about you."

"About me? What on earth for?"

"Well, there was that government guy, right?"

Sue Ann felt the heat rise to her cheeks.

"Mark, wasn't it?"

"Yes. Mark."

"Mark, the heart shark. Afterward, you were a basket case. It took you a while to forget that lousy two-timer. Too long." Viv looked up, saw the misery in Sue Ann's face, and tisked in sympathy. "Of all my friends here in Southeast, Sue Ann, you were the one I lost sleep over."

"That's silly, Viv. I've done very well—"

"Don't get me wrong. You've accomplished a lot. Raising Serena, battling the bureaucracy in the Fisheries, boxing with your brother about how you should behave, whom you should date. You've had some good times, too, but there was always something wrong . . . like a bruise that's almost but not quite healed up, so you can still see blue under the skin."

Sue Ann felt a rise of irritation at having the years of her life capsulized like a bitter pill. "I've had my problems, I'll admit. The breakdown after Mark was rough, rough on everybody. But I'm stronger now. Even though I came up with the idea that I could use the Personals to find someone of my own, it's not as if I was lonely all the time. My work, my friends—"

"Dregs of the river, girl! You've been lonely for a good man since I've known you." Vivian straightened out Sue Ann's hand as if it were a trout on the cutting board. Sue Ann gave an exasperated sigh, which Vivian plowed over in her eagerness to scold. "And all that loneliness was your own fault," she said. "Wasting your youth, hiding your beauty, hoarding your affections like a miser. The world frightens you, and you've spent a lifetime protecting yourself."

Angered, Sue Ann pulled away her hand and clenched it. "And what about you, Viv? A good-looking woman like you. Hardworking, talented, loving. You could have been a wealthy society woman in the States or run a salon in Beverly Hills.

Instead, you're holed up in a one-horse town of thirty thousand people, working two jobs, selecting clients for the shop from a short list of close friends. That's not protecting yourself?''

"I'm a different kettle of fish." She took back the hand and brushed the file over a snag in the thumbnail. "I've had boyfriends, two husbands, a son—God rest his soul—and three careers with plenty of glitz and glamour. I've lived life."

"Yes, but loneliness . . . ?"

"I don't get lonely." Vivian paused, raised her eyes, and fired a look that held Sue Ann captive. "I adopted the world, Sue Ann. That's the difference between us. My friends and my work are enough. You? You've been running from the best life has to offer. I hope you've got the gumption to climb out of that rut. That's what I've wanted to tell you all these years."

There was enough truth in Vivian's analysis to send a streak of goosebumps over Sue Ann's back and arms. Her mouth pinched with the effort not to show her hurt, but Viv saw it anyway. She squeezed Sue Ann's hand and softened her tone. "You're a shy woman, sweetie. Private. You don't have a big appetite for social life, but you do have the need for intimacy. You want someone to share your life with. Serena and your brother have their own lives. Last December you finally realized it and placed the ad. I'm glad to see you breaking out of that shell of yours and doing something about getting what you want. Don't let your fears stand in the way."

"Oh, Viv." She sighed in agreement. "You read me so well. But what about you? Don't you ever want a man? Sexually or emotionally or anything?"

Viv busied herself with the manicure. "Women your age crave closeness. I don't need that anymore."

Frustrated with the vague answer, Sue Ann pressed. "Don't you miss that crazy feeling that makes your heart leap when the man you love has been gone for a while and you get back together?"

Vivian shrugged. "If I found someone, I might get into it."

"You don't sound very convincing."

"Face facts. The odds of a woman my age finding Mr. Wonderful are pretty slim. Even you, with all your assets, had to go outside to find the right guy. And I've got seventeen years on you. Anyway, finding a man isn't my focus in life.''

"Jerry's widowed ex-partner Clint Moss is coming to the wedding."

"Just like a reformed smoker," she quipped, grinning. "You quit, and you think the whole world should quit. Or, in this case, start finding love."

Thinking that Viv wasn't entirely immune to the possibility of romance, Sue Ann angled around to see what was on television. It was a game show. She watched a young black woman win the jackpot. "I hear Clint's dating but not serious about anyone," she said casually, baiting Vivian, who remained silent.

The jackpot winner was hugging the game-show host. The camera panned the audience. A good-looking man stepped out of the crowd and came running up on stage to embrace the winner. Husband or lover, Sue Ann thought, waiting for Vivian to respond to the bait about Jerry's friend. How absolutely joyous they looked, embracing. How safe.

Society was structured in pairs: husband/wife, mother/daughter, friend/friend. Alone, you were vulnerable, an oddity to the rest of the world. Even though loving someone had held the most potential for hurt—enough hurt to prevent her from grasping happiness for herself, before this year—she'd always felt herself to be slightly outside the mainstream as a single woman. Single women were seen by other women to be a threat to otherwise stable marriages; she'd read the questions in wives' eyes a thousand times, at parties, P.T.A. meetings, picnics. I know you're lonely, those sharp looks would say, but hands off *my* man!

And many of the husbands, perhaps innocently, promoted their wives' insecurities by flirting, by commenting about the excitement of single life, and by outright lechery. In the men's eyes, at least symbolically, she was fair game for flirtations because no man had stamped her as his. While she resented the ownership that implied, she chaffed under their assumptions.

Only the close rapport she'd shared with Serena, or with Eric when she was with him at public outings, had eased Sue Ann's feeling she was the odd woman out. Didn't Viv ever feel the pressure?

The credits rolled across the TV screen, and Sue Ann turned around, wondering if she should probe her friend's deeper feelings. Perhaps Viv had a magic formula for dealing with society's typecasting of a woman.

Vivian squeezed some hand cream into her palm, warmed it by rubbing her hands, then smoothed it on Sue Ann's forearms. She began to massage the atrophied muscles of the scarred arm, and Sue Ann closed her eyes, relaxing. It was her favorite part of the manicure. In a moment, Viv said, "You've got a lot more strength in this arm than you used to have. The massages have done some good."

"Mmm," Sue Ann murmured.

Viv bent back the fingers of the hand, pressing and manipulating and stretching the muscles. Sue Ann was listening to the drone of the television when Viv said, "How old is he?"

She suppressed a smile. "Who?"

"Who were we talking about? The partner, what's-his-name."

"Clint?" Sue Ann bathed her friend in an innocent stare. "About fifty-eight, I expect. Thirteen years older than Jerry. Old friend of the family. Rock of Gibraltar, Jerry says."

"An accountant." She scoffed. "Probably an old stick-in-the-mud."

"Hey." Sue Ann sat up straight. "You only need to know one good one to realize they're not all glued to a slide rule." Sue Ann tried to catch Viv's glance, but the redhead was sorting through bottles of polish. "The dusty rose," Sue Ann said, pointing. "You're so clever at changing the subject."

As Viv removed the cream from Sue Ann's fingernails, then painted them with a clear base coat followed by the pink, Sue Ann admired her friend's self-containment. In all the years between serious relationships, Sue Ann had always longed for the security that came from loving a man she admired. No matter how fulfilling her life had been, Viv was right, she'd been lonely for the companionship and love of a mate.

"Sometimes they want to own you," Viv said quietly.

Sue Ann came mentally to attention but said nothing.

"I'm too independent now."

Sue Ann frowned. "So am I. Are you saying independent women can't be happy in love?"

"It'll have to be dealt with, is all. You have to keep up your own interests to be fulfilled and to keep the spark of his attention. But you also have to let your man know you're dependent on him. They like that protectiveness feeling."

She bit her lip. "Viv, what if *I* feel the protectiveness feeling, because I think he might not be capable? What if he's more vulnerable than protective?"

"Are you trying to tell me Prince Charming has a flaw?"

"Just . . . he gives too much."

Viv's glance came up sharply. "That's a flaw?"

"Well, I mean, he's good-humored and loving and very patient with Eric. But he offered me this huge sum of money when he first got here. Really huge. And he gave me all these emotion-charged gifts—his grandmother's china, his mom's silver wedding-picture frame—things he cherishes. And certain things have happened. You know, subtle things."

Viv finished with the polish, capped the bottle. "And . . . ?"

"And he seems to be trying too hard to convince me. He almost seems desperate to lock me in."

"There's always a price tag, sweetie. What's his?"

"Exactly my question. Now he's brought me this document that doesn't list our assets or anything. All it says is that what's his is his and what's mine is mine unless we earn it together after we're married."

"That's a really basic premarital agreement."

"I know. But why give me so much, then protect himself that way? Why doesn't he just wait to see how we get along?" She frowned. "I get the feeling he's trying to lock me in, and it makes me nervous."

"If you weren't ready for the commitment, Sue Ann, why did you set the wedding date?"

Sue Ann stared. Wasn't she ready? Hadn't she hated the oppression of single life—the loneliness, the typecasting—and done something to end it? But had she been right to stick so tightly to her goal; had it blinded her?

"Well?" Viv asked, rolling her shoulder as if to loosen cramped muscles.

Sue Ann shook her head in confusion. "I felt so ready for marriage all year, especially after Jerry and I started really communicating. You know, finding things to like about each other. The relationship seemed so..." She waved, unable to express what she meant.

Viv filled in the blank. "Safe?"

"Yes," she sighed.

"And then the real Harrison Ford showed up."

There was a silence full of surprise and self-recognition. It was true; in person, Jerry was so *real*. So full of bigger-than-life appetites, opinions, desires—and faults.

"Well," said her friend, tucking her nail file into her pocket and aligning the bottles along the edge of the table, "my advice to you is to get rid of all your worries and grab on to love. I never met anyone more in need of it than you."

"But what about my questions, Viv?"

"Ask *him* the questions, silly girl. Work these things out together. And don't let his answers stand in your way. He's a good man or you wouldn't be bringing him home. Trust your instincts."

"Yes," Sue Ann agreed, looking off. Confidence began to build in her, and as she thought about the moment he would come into her arms tonight, her body felt like a wind tunnel full of excitement. *Ask him,* she thought. *And believe in him.*

Chapter Seven

Sweeping aside the full mid-calf-length skirt of her pink dress, Sue Ann picked up another split log and fed it into the pot-bellied stove. Sparks popped through the coal grate. Jumping back, she stamped at them with her heeled satin shoe. At this rate, she'd be charred and frazzled by the time Jerry finally showed up, she thought in frustration. Using a poker to shove the lid of the stovetop back into place, she stood the rod in its holder, stepped off the brick hearth, and leaned against a knotty-pine wall.

Dusting her hands, she glanced at her watch. Three hours, thirteen minutes late. Where was he? Should she give in to anger and hurt, or be worried about him?

Again she recapped what she knew. Jerry wasn't at the hotel, and he wasn't at Mel's. She'd called. And she'd left a message on Brenda's phone recorder asking Mel to call if he came by. Not knowing who else had gone in the shooting party, she'd run out of leads and called the hospital. Neither Jerry nor Mel had been admitted.

It was possible they'd stopped by a bar to play pool and throw down a few beers. Mel liked his beer. And hadn't Jerry often said he liked a good time? But she didn't want to think about what it said for his character if he'd stood her up on their first night at the cabin.

"Left at the altar with a calling card in my hand," wailed a country singer on the radio. She didn't need *that* fear wearing away her confidence.

Circling the loft stairs, Sue Ann went to a wall lined with books and sophisticated entertainment equipment. The lights and controls marked the systems as high tech, an array of electronic marvels most media-hungry Alaskans would have given their annual moose tag to own, and she was proud of it: a VCR, a color TV linked to an eight-foot satellite dish outside, a computer that spoke to her in a suave male voice and generated color graphics that had spiffed up her Fisheries reports, and a music system so complicated it had taken a technician three trips out to the cabin before he had gotten the bugs worked out.

Even the sound system was a reminder that her special evening with Jerry was all but ruined. She'd been looking forward to his appreciation of the fact that, last June, when she'd finally made up her mind to marry him, she'd bought a compact disc player and a collection of his favorite big band and rock 'n' roll hits, all digitally reproduced from original forties-through-sixties recordings. It was her gift to him to help ensure he would not grow restless, living almost an hour's drive from town. She'd planned to surprise him tonight, show him who she was, who he was marrying. Now she wondered if she'd wasted her money and effort. Maybe nothing she did would hold him.

Quickly she tapped the preset buttons until light jazz played over her senses.

Walking to the picture windows, she gazed out without seeing the black shadow lines between the planks of the porch. Nor did she focus on the bough of the great spruce that framed, in daylight, the bay and the distant white peaks of the Chilkoots. What she did see in the glass was a reflection of the oak table in the dining nook, Jerry's grandmother's rose-patterned china artfully arranged for two, sprigs of evergreen in the bud vases and red candles waiting to be lit. And she wanted him to come home, to keep the jackals of the past from tearing her to shreds.

The telephone rang and she darted for it, answering breathlessly.

"Sue Ann, Teech here," said her friend from Phoenix, Arizona, whom she'd met at a resources convention in Canada. "Only got a second. I'm flying to Brazil tonight."

The disappointment at not hearing Jerry's voice made it easy to keep the amenities to a minimum. She expressed pleasure at Teech's call and said she was looking forward to seeing him before the wedding.

"That's why I'm calling, Sue Ann. I'll be locked into negotiations in Brazil till the first of the year. Two multinational companies have their eye on an opal mine that's up for sale, and I want it. I've got to stay on it. I was going to send the ring you ordered. I will, if it gets here in time."

"If?" she said, trying to keep the sudden panic from her voice.

"I loaned out the original I had with me in Canada, the one you liked so much. The woman who wanted a look at it had all her holdings frozen in a court dispute. I'm assured the ring will be released to my man Stone in time to copy the design and express-mail it to you, but the timing might be close. If need be, I'll send Stone up with it."

Sue Ann barely heard his explanations and assurances. Somehow she remembered to wish Teech luck in Brazil and hung up, her thoughts in chaos.

She must have the ring. People hereabouts had to know— Know what? she faltered. That she and Jerry were important, with him wearing a white-gold-and-platinum ring set with a one-karat diamond of superior clarity? What was she trying to prove, draining her savings to give him a ring like that?

But she knew . . . the ring was a symbol of respectability.

Suddenly, involuntarily, she shuddered.

To admit the ring stood for respectability was to remember a time when she'd lost her reputation. The events of that devastating Easter Sunday, ten years earlier, came like a thundering phantom from her memory, and she ran to the windows, afraid to remember.

Hugging herself, trying to hold herself together, she faced the threat and began it—the exhumation of Mark's ghost.

She recalled the Easter Sunday she and Mark had been at church. A reporter waiting for him on the steps outside had been de rigueur . . .

Mark's dark good looks and natty clothes had always been a source of pride to her. Mark was flashy, friendly; he drew women and reporters the way a new jet draws test pilots. His mind was razor-sharp, too, so the movers and shakers in Alaskan politics respected him. There was always a furor when he was around, always excitement. Who wouldn't love Mark when, on top of everything else, his charm could melt the polar icecap?

After lying in state for so many years following Bill's death, Sue Ann had breathed Mark's excitement as pure oxygen and had come back to life.

How circumspect they'd been, she and Mark. As planned, he appeared once a month at the Baranoff to dine with one of several respectable women—a wealthy widow who was politically connected, a female newspaper executive, and yes, once in a while, Sue Ann: single parent, widowed, recently promoted to section assistant in a government office (and cleaning homes on the weekends to make ends meet, but they kept that a secret, too). Their affair was very hush-hush, of course, because of Mark's association with the governor—and because Mark was slated by his party to hold public office someday.

How circumspect they'd been, Sue Ann thought now, and how naive she'd been to think Mark was only having dinner with the other women.

That Easter Sunday, the young reporter had set her straight. He'd met them outside the doors of the church and asked Mark embarrassing questions about his personal life, and had made sly innuendos about the work Sue Ann was doing in the respectable homes of the city—hooking, perhaps? He'd printed his questions, his facts, his innuendos the next day, along with quotes from obscure witnesses and a terse denial from the governor.

If Mark hadn't chosen a senator's wife, played with her, used her as he had the other "public" women he'd seen and bedded, he might have salvaged his career. But the political machine had been tarnished by his James Bond intrigues, and they'd had to ruin him completely to weather the scandal. They'd ruined Sue Ann's life in the process.

The remembrances floated through her mind as she stood by the window, hugging herself. Images of the reporter's snide smile, Mark's look of horror, of guilt, his denials. *Sue Ann, don't believe this idiot. Those women were just a front, please,*

baby, believe in me. And images after that Sunday, images of
sorrow, shame, pain, running together to convulse a heart that
tried to open to him but couldn't, because she had endured so
much, lost so much.

When he'd called that last time, he had come calling on a
desolate, unfeeling heart. *Sue Ann, I'm leaving Alaska this
afternoon. Won't be back, but if you ever need anything—* She
couldn't hear his hoarse, choked pleas, not really. *Please,
baby, forgive me. Let me help you if you can't make it alone.
Sue Ann, I-I'll never stop watching out for you. Least I can do.
Still have some friends in Juneau. Won't contact you—oh,
God, Sue Ann, I'll always love you....*

Once, five years ago, Mel had told her he'd run into someone who said Mark was clerking in an accounting firm in
Washington, D.C.—like a washed-up actor scrubbing floors
in a Hollywood studio, she thought. Mel said Mark had asked
about a woman just like Sue Ann, a tall blonde with a dark-
haired daughter. She'd pretended not to hear Mel, and he'd
never mentioned Mark again. She'd buried all but the pain of
betrayal.

Easter Sunday. Mark. *Never stop watching out for you.* Last
January. The postmark on the envelope containing the conditions of the legacy: Washington, D.C.

Chilled by premonition, Sue Ann hurried to the stove, held
out her hands. They shook as the questions pounded her.

Was it Mark, sending her the legacy? Was she risking the
trust of her future husband and her dear brother because a
bastard from the past wanted to see her married to relieve his
own guilt? The possibility was horrifying. No, it was too far-
fetched, she thought, rubbing her hands to warm them.

There was no way to know who the money was from until
after the wedding, and if she found out it was from Mark,
she'd throw it back in his face.

The money wasn't the important issue in her life, anyway.
It was the ring that had sent her into that Pandora's box of
memories. Well, she'd done it, gone in and looked at them—
and survived it. She felt better, stronger, more certain of herself. The ring mattered, mattered very much, but her missing
fiancé mattered more. Finding him and learning why he gave
and took like the tide mattered above all.

She'd have a glass of wine, she decided; it might take the edge off her desire to throttle him when he gave his excuses for not showing up.

Crossing the rag rug that flowed in an oval from the picture windows to the brick hearth and from the bookcase to the dining alcove, she skirted the table, her heels tapping on oak flooring. She pushed open a set of café doors. The sweet earthy scent of roast venison greeted her. Ignoring the baking pan with its crisp delicacy perched like a pagan crown on the stovetop, she went to the counter where the wine bottle and two crystal goblets winked at her. Mocked her.

Resolutely she took up a goblet, uncorked the wine and poured. She inhaled the piquant fumes of an eleven-year-old California cabernet. Damn him, she thought, and took a sip, then a generous swallow. The wine was dry and robust; no bite, only a lingering musty flavor that reminded her of the forest on a sunny day. Damn him that he wasn't sharing this pleasure with her now.

As she was taking another sip, the telephone rang. Sue Ann jumped, set down her wine, and burst through the café doors at a run. She slowed in the narrow channel between the stove and the end table, grabbed the lampshade to steady it because she'd almost tipped over the lamp, then rushed around the chair and came to a halt facing the telephone. It shrilled again.

"All right," she said, smoothing her dress as if Jerry could see the cling of lace against her breasts. *It could have been car trouble,* she told herself. *Someone's hunting license blew out of the car window and had to be found. Anything. Give him the benefit of the doubt. Trust him. He's not Mark . . .*

On the fourth ring she picked up the receiver and said hello.

"Sue Ann, Laura. Is Eric there?"

She slumped in disappointment. "Eric? No, was he coming out?" She sent a wild glance around the room—its red plaid blankets, knotty-pine walls, muted lighting, unlit candlelight dinner for two. The cozy scene was normal, yet tonight it seemed seductive. Eric would ruin it with disparaging remarks about a woman's romantic wiles. In her present mood, they would have a terrible fight. "I—wasn't expecting Eric. I was having a dinner for Jerry."

"Damn." Laura choked out a worried breath. "He was due back at seven."

"Tell me about it," Sue Ann said with exasperation. "Jerry's almost four hours late. He and Mel and a couple of the guys from Fisheries went out to the shooting range on Montana Creek Road."

"I know," Laura said. "Eric went with them."

"Eric?"

"Yes. When it comes to you and Jerry, he's just lost all his reason. Last night he kept up a tirade for an hour about how that 'city slicker' was going to ruin your life."

"He has no right to say that," she said sharply. "It's my life."

"Sue Ann, he knows that. He's just so traditional, and he's used to watching out for you. The circumstances of your engagement are counter to everything he wanted for you. You can't turn off a habit that's been formed over twenty years of hard use."

"But don't you see, Laura? If Eric keeps giving me guff about Jerry, we'll never be a family again." Letting out an impatient breath, Sue Ann stood up. "Anyway, we can't really deal with that now, Laura. We've got to figure out where they are."

"Sue Ann..." Laura's usually soft voice rose with increasing worry. "Today Eric came home for lunch, muttered something about 'showing up that Teal dude for what he was' and went out with his 30-06. It was ego talking, not the killer instinct, but still... He skipped work for the afternoon—*now*, of all times, when the mining contract is so important to us."

The jazz from the stereo struck odd discordant notes, as if the D.J. had put a penny on the record to slow it down. It disturbed Sue Ann's concentration. She tried to think of what to do. *Calm down Laura first,* she thought. *Get some perspective.*

"Mel and Eric are absolutely reliable when it comes to guns," Sue Ann said. "You know how no-nonsense they are in the woods."

"I know, I know. But why are they so late?"

"Laura, we can't panic."

"I'm not." But her voice still had a soprano edge.

"All right, listen. We'll make some phone calls. I've already called the hospital, but I'll call them again. You call the fire department and the police. We'll get back to one another in, say, ten—"

She hesitated, listening. The jazz was all awry, distorted.

"Sue Ann?"

"Hold on, Laura."

The beat of drums, the clang of cymbals and the moan of a saxophone gave way to what surely must be the chorus of the Seven Dwarfs as they returned from work. Outside, Eric's baritone voice rose in a challenge, a jubilant raw challenge to whatever nightforce his brain had conjured in the darkness. She heard the clatter of one of the planks lining the trail. A curse, then coarse laughter.

"Dear God," she muttered, feeling the first streaks of anger. "Laura, I think they're here. And very drunk. Hold on while I see."

As she flung the receiver to the couch, her anger drew heat from the hours of self-examination, uncertainty and worry. The force of her fury drove her fast down the hallway. How dare Jerry disregard the importance of their first night at the cabin? Surely if he understood he'd "passed muster," he realized how significant her bringing him here was. The fury built as she palmed the latch—it stung her hand. She cursed, then used both hands to heave open the door. It slammed into her shoulder. She staggered as pain knifed down her bad arm. Cradling her shoulder, she hunched against the doorjamb and peered into the night, half-blinded by rage, pain and the sudden darkness.

Moonlight cast shadows on the planks and patches of snow. Damp wind from the inlet chilled her face.

As her vision sharpened, Sue Ann saw caricatures of men stumbling up her boardwalk. Coats hung lopsided. Breath shot from their mouths like steam expressed from the valves of a narrow-gauge train.

Unbelieving, Sue Ann watched Eric fling an arm over Jerry's shoulders. "Stlill-ll a bastard, Teal," her brother said, the words slurred. "Aren't 'cha? Huh?"

Jerry grinned crookedly. "Wrong!"

"No, I'm right!"

"Wrong!" Mel chimed from beneath Eric's other arm.

"You tell 'im, Mel," Jerry said. "I'm good-time-Charlie's bes' buddy."

Holding each other upright, they howled, the laughter ricocheting through the trees.

Despite a residual trembling in her legs, Sue Ann felt a nudge of exhilaration. The camaraderie of the men was like a benediction over her coming marriage. Could she trust what she saw? It was so stunning to see Eric hugging Jerry that she could only stand staring in the doorway, fifteen feet away from the miracle, her resentment receding.

Sue Ann closed the door a little and hurried back to the telephone. "All three of them, soused," she announced to Laura. "They'll have to fight over who gets the couch."

"You're kidding, Sue." Calm had returned to Laura's voice, and she tisked in sympathy. "They loused up your dinner and now you've got to listen to their snoring all night? I'm really sorry."

"I'm trying to dredge up some righteous indignation, Laura, and you're helping. But they're getting along so well, maybe the sacrifice of one private dinner-for-two will have been worth it."

"Eric and Jerry?"

"Bosom buddies."

"I'll be amazed if it lasts. You know Eric."

"Right you are. I'd better go give them a hand before they tear the railing off the back stairway. And if Eric has the nerve to remember he hates Jerry in the morning, they'll be sorry they left the guns wherever they left them. I'll make full use of my own war chest."

Laura chuckled. "At least they're okay."

Sue Ann felt a warmth go through her. "Yes," she said quietly. "Alaska must have been in a good mood today. Lucky us. Call you tomorrow, Laura."

They hung up just as heavy boots hit the tiles in the entry. The door slammed, shaking the floor. A curse tore through the house. Then she heard Jerry's voice. "Shh-hhh! Don't cuss in the presence of ladies, man. Bad taste."

"Ladies?" Mel sounded happy, clomping down the hallway. "Where they at?"

Sue Ann stood near the recliner, her hands on her hips. Jerry was the first to stride into sight, mimicking, "'Ladies. Where they at?'" He saw her and wavered to a standstill. He pointed. "There they are. Hi, babe!"

"Hi yourself, babe. Back from the wars so soon?"

"Wars?"

"Never mind. How about some coffee?"

"Sheesh. I mean, yesh."

"Where's the car, Jerry?"

He grinned. "Taxshi."

"Ah. Good. You took a taxi."

"Yesh."

Mel and Eric bumped into Jerry, shoving him forward. Sue Ann automatically reached out for him. He swept her up in the chilled sleeves of his coat and pressed an iceberg of a face against her cheek. "Hi, babe," he said again, the intimacy thick in his voice. "Shtill love me?"

"Love isn't the word for it," she muttered. But she hugged him quickly before letting him go. She ducked around to watch Mel and Eric lean against each other for balance and peek at her. "Ah," she said. "The Texas Rangers."

"She's mad," said Eric, jabbing a thumb in her direction. "Teal's in for it." He giggled. "Serve the bast—"

"Sh-hhh!" said Jerry. He stood back and brandished an arm toward Sue Ann. "Ladies."

Mel looked around, evidently searching for others.

"I've got to ask," said Sue Ann. "What was so important to celebrate that you ruined my dinner party?"

"Teal," said Eric, pointing at him. "I still don't trust the sum-bitch."

"Teal?" she asked in a saccharine tone.

"The lard tin," Eric said. "S'prized me."

Intelligible answers were only a remote possibility, but she was beginning to get some teeth into her anger. She snapped the lamp on high-beam, taking satisfaction from the fact that the men ducked and shielded their eyes. Her fists went back to her waist. "What about the lard tin?" she asked coolly.

"I shot it," said Jerry, beaming.

"Congratulations," she said dryly. "You stood me up for a lard tin."

He looked vaguely abashed. "You look beooo-tiful, sweet-heart."

"Sorry I can't return the compliment."

"Yesh, me too."

Mel came up and took a paternal grip on her good arm. "You don't unnerstand, Suzie."

"Agreed."

"Now, see, we had this five-gallon tin nailed down to this log. We ff-filled it w' sand and shot at it. Sand went every-where. Teal got ten straight bullzeyes. Bam, bam, bam—"

Despite her sense of injustice, a beam of pride sped through her.

"Eric said he was buying the beers," Mel finished. "See? You gotta crack shot for a husband and we gotta buddy. We oughta bought you a six-pack for bringin' him up here." He staggered to Jerry. "Ol' buddy." He grinned and clapped him on the back, sending him toward Sue Ann.

"Rest yourselves, gentlemen," she said, hooking Jerry's arm and leading him to the easy chair to settle him in. She dragged Eric by the elbow until she had him hovering over the far end of the couch. "Sit," she ordered.

"Still bossy." Her brother made a disagreeable face but slithered down, one foot bent awkwardly and the other shooting straight out. Dancing out of the way, she headed for Mel. But he sidestepped her with amazing agility and flung himself into the corner of the couch nearest Jerry.

Satisfied, Sue Ann said, "Coffee," and headed for the kitchen.

In half an hour, she'd served them coffee, roast-venison sandwiches and chocolate cake. Then she covered them with blankets and banked the fire in the stove. Eric was stretched out on the rug and beginning to rattle the rafters with snores. Jerry and Mel, sleeping in the chair and on the couch, respec-tively, were quiet. Sue Ann crossed to the stereo and turned off the music, then returned to Jerry.

For a moment she stared down at him. Swaddled in a green comforter and slumped in the armchair, he still emanated a life-force that called to Sue Ann's womanhood. The steel-gray hair at his temples gleamed in the lamplight. His black lashes fringed high cheekbones. Age lines fanned from his eyes, and deep grooves channeled his mouth. Stubble smudged his angular jaw. In that face she saw vulnerability, too, and was moved.

"Damn you for spoiling our first date," she whispered, and bent down to brush his cheek in a gentle kiss.

Aching a little at the sight of him in her home, she climbed the stairs to the loft. Why the strange pull in her heart to see Jerry vulnerable, she wondered, changing to a cotton nightdress and sliding into the warm waterbed with the antique frame. From a need to nurture because Serena was gone? But she didn't want to be a mother figure to Jerry. Weren't they different feelings, nurturing versus loving a man? Or were they such closely woven urges a woman could not help mixing the two?

There was a real difference about her life these days, she reflected. For the first time in nearly two decades, she was examining the underpinnings of her beliefs, exposing her past and attempting to understand what made her happy. Did Jerry inspire that kind of depth in her? Or, in attempting to avoid a wintry widowhood, was she driving herself to plumb the depths of her ability to give and receive love? Even asking the question amazed her. She'd always plodded on without wondering why.

Correction. Since Bill's death—until last Christmas—she'd considered life nothing more than an endless dim tunnel through which she was forced to plod.

Chilled by her own cynicism, she pulled the covers high around her chin. Jerry was the light and sunshine. Deliverance. No wonder she'd expected him to be a saint.

Twisting into a fetal position, Sue Ann knotted her fists and vowed not to put such a burden on him. He was a man, with his own faults and his own needs. *"Work it out."* That had been Vivian's advice. She must not sabotage her own happiness.

Perhaps the real benefit of her relationship with Jerry, she mused, was the opportunity to know herself. If he gave her that chance, it would be an incredible gift.

For a while she lay listening, recognizing Jerry's snore although she'd never heard it before, and slipping lazily into her own twilight.

GRAY LIGHT SLID DOWN through the east window of the loft, shrouding the cherry-wood bedroom set, the braided rug, the balcony overlooking the living room.

Her body still damp from the shower and gleaming in the pearly light, Sue Ann stood peering over the rail, her knuckles whitening. She suspected she was alone in the cabin.

"Jerry?" she called.

She listened to the crackle of the fire someone had built in the potbellied stove. She smelled the nutty scent of coffee mingled with traces of wood smoke. It was the aroma of coffee that had propelled her out of bed and rapidly into the shower, so she could get downstairs and talk to Jerry.

"Jerry?" she said. Grabbing the damp towel off the bed and wrapping herself in it, Sue Ann ran downstairs, looked in all the rooms, looked outside, came back into the living room. No Jerry.

Sue Ann's shoulders sagged, and in this moment, knowing he'd run out on her, she came close to hating the cabin for its isolation. It should have held the two of them this morning. Instead it held only her.

She felt as a sport fisher must feel after fighting a giant marlin for six hours, until the stomach burned and the shoulders screamed for rest, only to lose the big fish off the gaff alongside the boat. The sense of disbelief must be profound, she thought. And the regret—a long, deep ache.

Overnight, the question of Jerry's reliability had become a proven flaw. It hurt to know he hadn't even waited until the bloom was off the marriage before showing he didn't really give a damn—or, worse, that he was a coward. And her regret came largely because she knew herself; she'd build another ring of protection around herself, and he'd find it difficult to tear it away to find her forgiveness. That was what she'd done after Mark.

"Damn you, Jerry Teal," she shouted. Anger flushed her like a sudden storm. She'd die a dried-up old tree frog before she'd let him break her heart.

The thought sent her into action. Dashing from room to room, she began exorcising him from her life.

She slammed through the café doors to the kitchen, choked out, "Gone, and good riddance!" and sent the open bottle of wine crashing into the sink. It broke, splashing red liquid over the tiles. Heedless, she plowed back into the dining room.

His grandmother's china gleamed from the table, reminding her that she'd planned to get rid of Eric and Mel so she could share a private breakfast with Jerry and get her fears laid to rest once and for all. But they'd stolen that moment from her—three little boys sneaking out before daybreak to escape the tongue-lashing they deserved. To top it off, they'd tried to appease her inevitable anger with token niceties—coffee, the fire—niceties she'd never had before because she'd been the one in charge, the mother, the single woman. Their attempt to buy her off infuriated her. She could not be bought that cheaply. It was emotion that mattered. Caring. Consideration. *Being there.*

She grabbed a coffee cup, but its fragility stunned her, and she hesitated. She thought of the loving use to which the cup had been put by a woman who had loved her mate to sentimental distraction. And she remembered, though it hurt, what the china meant to Jerry. The saucer rattled when she put down the cup. She'd mail Jerry's memories back in a box.

Undaunted by her decision to save the china, she stomped down the hall to the guest bathroom. She gathered the red toothbrush and the scented shower soap she'd bought him. Someone had used them. Irritated, she tossed the items into the wastebasket, muttering, "Eric was right, he was right about you. You're just out for a good time."

A hot moisture stung her eyes. She wiped it away with her fist and ran to the back door. Wincing at the pain that coursed down her arm when she flung it open, she shouted to the empty path, "Coward! I'll never marry you."

It was useless bravado, just as it had been when she'd sent her ad to the *L.A. Times.* She'd thought she could send out for happiness, like pizza—hold the heartache, please. But the mail-order business wasn't meant for people. They were too unpredictable; the truth-in-advertising laws didn't apply. Jerry might have looked great on paper, but the real item was a rip-off.

The humiliation of having come this far with a romance she'd been fool enough to believe in was still a tight knot in her stomach. She was panting from her rampage, yet the anger and hurt suffused her with energy, with the need to hurt back.

She slammed the door, wadded up the towel. Cocking back her throwing arm, she raced to the foot of the stairs and heaved the towel at the picture window. ''Go to hell, Jerry Teal,'' she yelled.

And then Sue Ann stopped dead still.

Out on the porch the man she'd just damned stared at her as if she'd sprouted horns and a forked tail. Clusters of yellow seaweed filled his hands and trailed over his arms. He'd been walking on the beach.

And she was naked in the throes of a tantrum.

Chapter Eight

The sight of Sue Ann's body, white and curved and poised with the passion of a Michelangelo sculpture against the dimness of the hallway, sent a streak of desire through Jerry. It was so unexpected, her nakedness. So sharply sexual. Such a contrast to her usually reserved womanhood.

The heat gathered in him, and he welcomed the slight hardness because he had wanted Sue Ann from the first moment he'd seen her at the airport. He'd been celibate since agreeing to marry her, and these past weeks, wooing her, bringing her to the brink and back again, feeling her tremble beneath his hands, letting her cool—all of it so she would be eager for him on their wedding night—had severely tested his control. Now, as he stood staring at her, his patience fled and his willpower shattered. His own need was raw. He was filled with guilt about last night, filled with longing and, at seeing her naked, filled with a strange power. If she would love him now . . .

But his arms brimmed with the seaweed he'd gathered when he'd walked to clear his head this morning. His hands were gritty with sand. Bad timing, he cursed inwardly, moving his shoulders impatiently.

A few ribbons of seaweed rustled to the porch. Sue Ann watched them fall, then looked again at his face.

And it was in that moment that Jerry forgot his own needs.

Framed by a mass of ringlets the color of dark honey, her features were molten with emotion. Her expressions had bolted from despair and anger to shock, and now embarrassment. Don't be ashamed, he wanted to tell her through the glass. And don't hide behind that mask of control, where nothing honest shows, and where I can't see that you care.

For that was it: he'd found, in mere half seconds, not just the woman to whom he'd given his faithfulness and his future, but the woman he would love. A woman of passion and caring and depth. She'd taken care of him last night, when he hadn't deserved it. She had compassion. Strength and compassion. And now, fire.

For the first time since he'd known her, Jerry understood what lay beneath her reserve. He had seen the kaleidoscope of feelings. He did not fully understand why all her fire and spirit lay banked like last night's coals most of the time—something about fear—but the sparks were there, waiting to be kindled, and her needs tapped his own compassion.

He had hurt her. How could he transform her vulnerability into trust? Somehow he had to try.

The seaweed slithered from his hands as he took a step toward the door. She began to turn toward the stairs.

She'd put the mask back on, he knew, panicking at the thought of what he would lose if he couldn't gain her trust.

"Sue Ann," he called—more a command than anything, but it couldn't be helped. Dusting his hands, he strode to the door. The hinges creaked when he pulled it open. Sue Ann had one foot on the stairs, her thigh muscles flexed to bolt; and the curve of her leg went like a photograph to his brain, where the image transfused his desire and shortened his breath.

"Wait," he said, wondering for the first time at the depth of her anger. Had she thought he'd walked out on her without facing what he'd done yesterday? *Go to hell, Jerry Teal,* she'd shouted. Her face was in shadow, the profile firming up, but it would not work this time. He must break through her wall of self-protection.

He came to her and grasped her shoulder. She winced. "Sorry," he murmured, turning her gently. "I didn't realize your bad arm was still sensitive."

"Normally it isn't," she said in a shaky voice. "I bumped into something yesterday."

She was staring at the thread that held his pocket to the blue plaid shirt, staring hard at it, her cheeks pink. He could see, below her chin, white globes traced faintly with veins—the most enticing breasts he thought he'd ever seen: mature, full, and far more beautiful than he'd expected of a woman of forty—and his nearness, or perhaps her earlier anger, had made tempting pink buds of the nipples.

A craving urged him to taste her, but it was ridiculous, the timing, the inappropriateness of his desire, her own awkwardness. She was embarrassed and vulnerable. Moved, he bent to brush her forehead with his lips—appreciating the brief soft press of her breasts against his chest as he straightened.

And then the surprise—the sudden movement she made to put her arms around his neck. With a low cry she pressed those full breasts and lovely rounded hips against him. His body flushed with the contact. Involuntarily, as he enclosed her slim waist, his eyes closed and a hoarse sound grated from his throat.

"I thought you'd gone," she murmured against his collar.

"No," he said, his voice scratchy. "I'm not a fool. Not sometimes."

"I called you a coward."

The word struck him coldly. And guilt made him silent.

"I'm sorry," she whispered.

The guilt lurched through him. He didn't trust himself to admit she was right about him. He wanted her trust without being willing to give it back. He couldn't give her honesty, not about whatever had kept him away last night, the—what?— fear that she needed him too much? He could barely understand it, let alone explain it to someone else. He nuzzled her damp hair. An air-and-honey scent, like that from the patch of lily of the valley he'd stopped to let his mother pick the spring they'd gone back to the old farm in New Hampshire, drifted around them, and the cloying memory of duty rose in him, quelling his arousal. He hated to feel the desire slip from him, but could not control the image of his mother's sickbed, the feeling of being trapped by her need, always her need, and by his own love for her, his duty...

His resentment.

He tightened his arms around Sue Ann. He must tell her something. What? "I'm sorry, too," he said. "About last night. I knew how much it meant to you to have Eric's acceptance. I stayed, worked on that. But it's no excuse."

As if she felt his withdrawal even though he hadn't stepped away, Sue Ann tightened her embrace. "I'm not perfect either," she said, rubbing her cheek against him. "I was angry about last night, and then when I couldn't find you this morning, I said awful things."

"Never mind," he managed. "Expectations. They freeze me up. My mother always expected me to be there for her, and she had no one else. But you're different. You're so self-contained most of the time. I—" he floundered "—if you can just give me a while to make it up to you for letting you down. Believe me, Sue Ann. I want years and years of our happiness."

She looked at him and he saw it—naked feeling for him, devotion he didn't deserve, forgiveness and hope and happiness and the possibility of love. That directness of hers, he thought, his breath catching. When she was being honest, the strength of that honesty—well, he didn't know if he could take it. The responsibility of it.

In that moment, before he could explain that he wanted to be worthy of her, that eventually she could lean against his love when she needed to, and that, finally, he would take his beginning steps toward honesty from her own strength, she bowed her head to his chest. She pressed kisses there, over and over.

Her warmth kindled him again, and he felt the imperceptible severing of mind and body. He found her lips, kissed her. She felt soft and yielding. Her passion came alive with an intensity that shocked him. She opened her mouth to him, teased him with her tongue, breathing a sweetness and hope and longing into him.

And something else formed to life in him. The need to dominate. He wanted his name on her lips and her body crying for him. He wanted everything, all of her, wanted to plunge into her and feel lost in her womanhood.

Probing with his tongue, he stoked her passion, fired it, let it fill him. They were moving together, tuning to each other, fitting, luring, giving. He kissed her throat. She swayed, and he caught her up hard. She gasped.

Covering her mouth, he spread his fingers over her warm back, caressing, demanding. A grain or two of sand rasped across her skin, and a sharp thrill went through him. The sand excited her, too. She twisted in his arms, fitting her hips to the ache in his thighs.

Like wildfire, the need leaped through him so hotly it seared the old guilts from his mind. His thighs felt thick and powerful, as if they alone could capture and tame her. His shoulders felt aggressive, and he pressed her down toward the rug. It was close to a miracle that she slid beneath him so willingly.

He struggled out of his jeans and boots, kissing her still, as she snapped open the buttons of his shirt. She peeled back the cotton from his shoulders. The pleasure of it was unbearable. A cloud of heat from the stove settled on his skin and mingled in his mind with the earthy scents of flowers and burning wood; the act of being undressed, and her ardor and the image of her willowy figure and her giving gaze, all pumping something wild through him.

She said something about questions. "My questions," she repeated. "I want to know . . ."

"Sue Ann," he said, his heart hammering. "Love me, give to me."

She moaned high in her throat. And suddenly they were silkiness and movement. Jerky movements and hesitations. Headlong rushes and exquisite tenderness—tenderness from her. He'd never, ever known a woman of such tactile versatility. Her lips on his face and chest and arms—any part of him within reach—were like the wings of a hummingbird. And the sharp prick of the hummingbird's beak, too, as she nipped him. Then she played a light forte with her fingertips, whispering touches over his chest and the hollow of his arm and the cords of his neck.

She was teaching him, he realized. Teaching him tenderness. Patience. And he did not know who would possess whom, who would dominate from sheer physical manipulation.

Frightened of her power, he pulled back. But she murmured his name and clung to him, whispering, "Let me give, Jerry. I'm your woman, your wife."

Somewhere beneath the old resentments hid the sensitive, caring Jerry Teal of his youth, and he groped for and found a shred of generosity. No expectation of reward. Just the simple joy of giving. A tenderness for a tenderness. He gave, ultimately, the hardest thing of all to give—part of his vulnerable self.

"I need you," he said.

"We need each other." And she wrapped him in her long shapely legs.

When he entered her, she welcomed and held him. He pushed deeper, and her fingers gripped his arms. She moaned.

Wait for her, he thought. *Wait, dammit*. Through slitted eyes, he gazed at her torso and saw the play of light on her skin. Satin skin. Gleaming like sunlight on a bird's wing. The soft stomach of a mature woman, held still as a pond in summer because he was still; the corded strength of a thousand workouts along her arms, waiting for him, waiting while he savored her. A bruise on her shoulder. The scars. Deep and white-ridged and connected to him by her passion. It was the scars that hooked into his compassion—the realization that she'd suffered, and had reasons to be afraid of life, and had trusted him to join her against everything she feared.

A softness for her urged him to speak. "I'll love you a long, long time, Sue Ann," he said, his voice husky.

And he watched her open her eyes to take in his wide chest and silver-tinted dark hair and the flush on his skin as he held himself still. Then she met his gaze. The light slanted across her face, lifting the highlights so her eyes glowed—or perhaps it was arousal, but her eyes were bright blue.

There was another flower in New Hampshire, he thought. Bluebells filled some meadows until it looked as if the sky and the earth had joined. He ached with pleasure to imagine Sue Ann lying among them, her eyes and the flowers and the sky all one color. A tremor shook him, and he throbbed for release.

Barely shifting her hips, Sue Ann gave him a slow, seductive smile. "Love me now, Jerry," she said softly. Reaching up, she took one of his nipples between a thumb and finger and twisted gently. A barb of desire shot through him. He plunged deeply into her.

They both cried out. Intense pleasure racked the center of his being, but he gritted his teeth and held on, master of his control and of her pleasure, until Sue Ann tensed, then cried out in release. He thrilled to the realization that he'd pleased

her. Then a white-hot flood crashed over him, pounding him
with its power, and from a great depth came the sound of his
voice.

LATER, as Jerry reached to the easy chair for a red blanket and
covered them, Sue Ann relished the light moving along his
shoulders. He was young-looking for forty-five, she thought.
Such powerful shoulders, with that frame of strong bones and
breadth of mature muscles. The sunlight coming from behind
him was kind; it haloed him.

The sun had emerged in the last hour—she didn't know exactly when—and she would have liked to take that walk on the
beach with Jerry, the walk she'd planned on the off-chance
their special evening might have lasted clear into this morning. Far up the inlet to the West, the Chilkoot Range would
shimmer above green islands, and underfoot the rocks would
be slippery with yellow seaweed. She had imagined them
clambering over the boulders where the stream poured into the
bay, peeking into the shallow cave farther on, hiking back
down the other way to watch the skiffs leave the float-dock in
the next cove.

Sue Ann remembered Jerry saying in one of his letters that
he loved to wander down to Santa Monica Pier after a storm
and watch the waves of the Pacific crash into the pilings. She
and Bill had done that. They had walked along with their arms
wrapped around each other, talking about raising a family.
That memory was like a legacy from Bill. She knew how it felt
to be in love and walk close to nature—to trust nature as if it
were a gigantic warm embrace. Only in the past year had she
found the courage to look back on those moments with Bill.
And because of the strength of the memories, she believed she
would find the courage to love Jerry.

They would walk together on the beach, she thought, snuggling against him. But right now their nest was too warm and
secure. Jerry tucked throw pillows around them. As he settled
next to her, he smiled, and she felt the warmth deep inside her.
Couples never made love perfectly the first time, she mar-
veled. They grew attuned through the practice of touching and
pleasing each other. But this first with Jerry seemed a miracle
of compatibility. His sensitivity, his virility; she'd had no

chance to ask questions or think about saving the moment for their wedding night. His need had seemed so overpowering, and come to think of it, her own need to feel unified with him so great, there could have been no conclusion but making love.

She touched his hair where the light went through it and turned the ends silver-gold. "Vivian would be shocked to know how poorly I took her advice," she said, reluctant to ask him the questions she should.

Tracing her cheek with his lips, he said, "Who's Vivian?"

"A friend." She held out her pink nails to him. "She's responsible for these."

"In that case, I'm in her debt and wouldn't dream of shocking her. Lovely clever hands, these." He kissed several fingertips.

She laughed. He was still feeling lovable. She couldn't just blurt out, Why did you try to give me all your money? It would ruin the mood, make him defensive. "She's going to play dresser to me and Laura and Tana," she said. "Speaking of the wedding, is your partner involved with anyone back home?"

He slid her pinkie finger into his mouth and pulled on it, sending streamers of pleasure through her. "Not anybody you could marry him to on such short notice." He grinned.

"Not marry him, silly. Vivian and Clint. I'm thinking of fixing the two of them up. Do you think he'd like Alaska? Is he as wonderful as you? Because he has to be special—"

Instead of answering, he shrugged under the blanket, propped himself above her using his arms as tent supports, and gave her only seconds to appreciate the reddish hue bathing his shoulders.

"Vivian deserves—" she tried.

He began to kiss her with delicate ritual.

"—a man as good as you," she got out before giving up her mouth to his kiss.

Already primed from the feast her body had so unexpectedly enjoyed after a very long time without love, her senses came alive, and she forgot matchmaking. Jerry rose away from her, teasing and seductive; she rose with him, following his mouth, arching her throat to his lips, urging him closer with nothing but the longing expressed by her body.

His hunger seemed to go to the depths of his soul, something she knew instinctively because she understood life and death and the need for love. Loving was a thing you did on the moment, a free thing, and questions and manipulations could rip it away. She wanted his hunger because it was in her, too. They were both battered by the outside world. But healed by unity, she knew, this hunger in them would be called love.

THEY WERE RAVENOUS and consumed the venison sandwiches as if they were nothing, eating on paper plates in the living room and looking at each other and giggling. Now, Jerry wearing his blue plaid shirt and jeans, Sue Ann in a pink sweater and matching cords, both of them barefoot, they were cleaning up the kitchen. They'd agreed on classical music, and Mozart filtered in through the café doors.

"This feels great," Sue Ann said, handing Jerry the sponge so he could wipe down the counter.

"What?"

"Putzing around the house with you."

Beginning to rub the tiles, he said, "Yeah, well. Don't get too crazy about it. I'm a man's man."

"Meaning it's beneath you to do the dishes?"

"Meaning I've always hated housework. This isn't so bad, you know, doing it once in a while with you. But I wouldn't want to be chained to the kitchen sink or anything."

Wiping the carving knife, she slid it into a drawer. "You never know. Could be exciting."

He stilled. "Now that you mention it . . ."

She swatted his back with the terry towel.

Spinning around, he roared and captured her. En route he tossed away the sponge. He pushed her against the counter and tried to put mock-passionate kisses all over her face. "Maybe I'll chain you to the kitchen sink," he said. "See how you like it."

"Uncle," she cried. She ducked back and forth, laughing. "I'll be so sore tomorrow I won't be able to get out of bed."

"Exactly where I want you."

"We haven't even had a chance to talk!"

"Why talk when we can love?"

"But I have a right to some answers, Jerry!"

He tensed. She hadn't meant to say it with such heart, but it was too late. His face lost its light, and the ravages of yesterday's drinking settled in heavy lines around his eyes and mouth. It hurt her to see how reality affected him. As if even that glimpse of his vulnerability were too much, he left her and switched off the kitchen light. He stood by the café doors, head and shoulders backlit by diffused light from the living room, his arm stretched out to the switch. She ached at the gloom that settled on him, head bowed, posture strangely defeated.

"Jerry—"

"No, you're right. We should talk."

"Oh, sweetheart." She came and hugged him. "We should be able to tell each other anything. It's safe, isn't it?"

"That depends on what you want to know."

She stiffened slightly. "I'm not an adversary, Jerry."

"Not now, no."

"Will I have to be one?"

"Depends."

"On what?"

"On what you need to know, Sue Ann. Women have their ways. They need—I don't know—" he waved "—things a man can't give, sometimes. Personal, soul-type things. It's scary."

She fought to understand and not feel hurt. "Like your wife? She wanted soul-type things from you?"

Silence. Then he said, "Yes. I felt she would suffocate me sometimes, and I stayed away."

There was something he wasn't saying, maybe couldn't admit. Was it his ex-wife—or was it something in him? Why had he stayed away last night? Their lovemaking had been incredible. His humor and generosity were priceless. Could she let all they did share be enough? It was such a gamble. Her career, her heart. What would loving him cost her?

"Jerry." She moved to stand in front of him. Taking his face in her hands, she made him look at her. It seemed to take a great deal of will, but he did it. Then she pulled her hands away and said, "I must know why you felt you had to give me that money."

"It was a gesture, Sue Ann. That's all."

"What did it mean?"

"I wanted you to know I meant we should have a long life together. I tried to tell you that." His gaze slid away to the stove, the floor.

She gambled. "All right. I accept that."

The unhappy gaze swung back to her; a dim light shone in the murky depths. "What else? If that's all, just the money—"

"The prenuptial agreement," she said.

He shrugged. "I had it drawn up on the advice of my partner. Clint said I was a fool not to have you sign it. I fluctuated back and forth. It was good advice, I guess. If you turned out to be a user, why, I'd stand a good chance of losing a great deal. But when I finally met you, I decided not to ask it of you. It was just a feeling I had."

"Why'd you change your mind?"

"Well, you seemed not to trust me. I don't know, maybe you had a fortune stashed away somewhere that you worried I might take someday."

A spike of guilt jabbed her heart. "F-fortune? You did it for me?"

"God, Sue Ann. It's so complicated." He rubbed his face, talked with his head averted. "Since my mother died," he said, "I've pretty much trusted only things that could be relegated to a financial document. Commitments of the emotional type were tied too closely to losing her, perhaps. I don't know. Maybe I burned out on caring." He took a breath. "Until I met you."

He pushed through the café doors and disappeared, while she braced her hand to stop the swinging door and stood in the dim kitchen, her heart pounding. She'd opened Pandora's box again. There were secrets writhing around them both. Jerry was afraid of emotional commitment. The gifts he gave were given because he was afraid to give himself. And she—she was afraid to trust, looking for guarantees, trying to control every detail so nothing would go wrong. Yet his attempts at honesty, and his tenderness, made her long to throw off her concerns and simply love him.

"Sue Ann?"

She jumped. "Coming."

Arranging her face to show none of her turmoil, she walked into the living room and found him lifting the lid of the pot-bellied stove. He shoved in three wedges of wood, poked around to settle them, slipped the lid back on. Sparks glowed on the bricks. She rushed forward, grabbed a log and smashed the sparks. "I keep meaning to get a new grate," she said.

"Where do you get one?"

"I have the address somewhere in my papers. There's a file in my bedroom."

He hung the poker in the rack. "You should move the woodpile back along the wall."

She glanced at the wood. The waist-high stack began about two feet from the back of the stove and ranged along the wall for about three feet. The grate was at the front of the stove, well away from the wood, but sparks were unpredictable. "You're probably right," she said.

"I'll move it for you," he said in a vague tone. His mind was on something else. He glanced outside. "It's beautiful here, Sue Ann. So peaceful."

The satisfaction of hearing his approval assuaged her. "The world goes away when I'm here, Jerry. It's not modern like your place in L.A. It's kind of buried in the woods. But do you think—that is, will you be able to feel at home here? Not too isolated?"

He smiled a little and indicated the book-case. "With all that gadgetry you showed me? With Eric to keep me on my toes—you to keep me warm? Bored? Are you kidding? Why, hell, Sue Ann, it's the kind of life I've always dreamed about."

The tension left her shoulders. She sighed. "Good. I'll try not to ask you too many questions that make you want to run away." He might ask her questions she couldn't answer. Maybe Viv was right. Maybe she ought to just trust her instincts about Jerry. She'd forget about giving him the third degree and simply trust him. She could do that, couldn't she? Based on what she knew of his goodness and his sensitivity?

He came close and hugged her shoulders. "We just need to give each other a chance to relax, huh?"

She glanced at his face. It was hopeful. "That's what we need to do," she said, smiling. "You want to see my favorite trout pond? You haven't begun to see the wonders of this place, Jerry."

"Talk's over?"

She nodded. "We're not great at playing court. But we are great at having fun. We do that awfully well."

"You know me, babe. I like a good time." He winked.

The questions went through her like hot wire—*Why* is having a good time such an issue with you? What does it hide? But all she said was, "Jerry, call me next time."

"Call?"

"The next time you want to keep 'having a good time,' and it affects our plans, call me. For some reason, having my plans botched makes me crazy. Unreasonably so. And I worry. I get paranoid. Then I want explanations. To save us all that, call. If you can do that, I think there'll be peace in this cabin."

"You got it, angel. Next time, I call."

Hope and excitement obliterated "next time." They would face life together, and the journey toward understanding and commitment was before them. When he nuzzled her neck, she hugged him and laughed aloud with happiness.

Chapter Nine

"You take care on that river," Sue Ann said, giving the brim of Jerry's red baseball cap a spirited little tug. "It can get nasty."

She'd have liked to come with him on this hunting trip. Jerry could see it in her wistful smile, the shadow of worry in her eyes as she stood beside him on the loading ramp, watching the others stow the last of the groceries and guns. He put his arm around her.

She hugged him hard and then shoved him gently away. "Go on," she said. "The freezer could use some moose steaks, and I've got to go see the preacher again, finish working out the vows."

He glanced away for a second, feeling a twinge of guilt. "We could have stayed. But I'm not much good at those kinds of details."

"I know."

Her soft tone made him look searchingly at her. "Anyway, it's sticking together that's important, babe, not a bunch of words."

"I'll leave out the 'obey' part, then." She grinned.

Jerry tweaked her nose, winked. "I like your spunk."

"We'll keep the part about 'cherish.'"

He kissed her cheek. She smelled like the carnations at the florist's shop they'd visited early this morning. Sometime during that glorious interlude at the cabin, he remembered thinking he'd have to cherish her to win her trust. "Yeah," he whispered. "Put 'cherish' in the vows. I cherish the heck out of you already."

Her smile brightened.

Beyond the ramp, one of the engines coughed, chugging into a deep-throated idle. Jerry glanced up. A woman flipped her blue scarf out of her way and nudged Sam Gord's white boat out into deeper water, where it floated between the land and the docks of the small boat harbor. Eric's friend Gord, in a yellow slicker, was hustling his three passengers into the seats under the cabin roof.

On the gravel bank near the water, Laura held the bowline of Eric's orange Saber Craft, while Eric grabbed the last rifle from Mel and yelled, "Fixing Sam's water pump cost us damned near an hour. Let's make the goodbyes short and sweet."

Sue Ann frowned at her brother. "Eric didn't call me back, Jerry. Busy, he told me a few minutes ago."

"He'll come around, Sue Ann. You'll see."

"He's just so hard to approach when he's mad. I hurt him. He's slow to forgive."

"Listen." Jerry took her by the shoulders. "Eric's got everything hitting him at once. Your marrying an outsider, pressure with the mine contract. He can't miss the hunt because he needs to fill the freezer. He just needs to get out into the woods and forget it all for a while."

"You think so?"

He nodded. "To ease your mind, I called L.A. Talked to Clint."

"And?"

"He'll bring a gray tux and burgundy cummerbund. Just in case—" He nodded his head toward Eric.

At that moment, Eric popped out of the back of the cabin and snapped, "We've got to make it across the bar at high tide. We'll be cutting it close. Let's go, let's go."

Mel climbed aboard.

Jerry turned back to Sue Ann. "Love, honor and cherish," he said, nudging her chin.

"Go on," she said, a perky smile replacing her gloom. "Get out of here. Go shoot a moose or something."

He wouldn't be shooting anything and she knew it, because he hadn't been able to obtain a permit, but he grinned and left her, and clambered aboard the boat.

As the men cruised down the harbor lane and around the point of a thickly forested peninsula called Juneau Island, Jerry saw the women gravitate together to watch the departure. And he thought: This is the life I've always wanted—just complicated enough to make it interesting, and just rugged enough to make a man and a woman hate to say goodbye.

It rained off and on during the two-hour boat ride out of Gastineau Channel and far up the Taku Inlet. The cold blustered down Jerry's back despite his wearing heavy wool shirts and Eric's spare orange all-weather coat. He sat wedged in the passenger seat surrounded by cartons of provisions. Behind him, Mel slumped in a seat facing the other way with his boots propped on a case of Moosehead Beer.

Across from Jerry, Eric drove the twenty-one-foot Saber Craft as if it were a wild thing, and sometimes it was, when a gust or a crosscurrent punched the bow off course. Then Eric's jaw jutted, and his big hands whipped the wheel around, power and confidence in every movement of his lean body. Sprigs of dark-blond hair poked out around his blue Peterbilt cap, giving him a home-grown look.

Several hundred yards to starboard, Sam Gord's Saber Craft planed the slate-green inlet. A plume of white water lifted off its wake. Both boats were flat out, the motors screaming.

The color of the water changed to milky green. Mel called to him, and Jerry swiveled around.

"Hut Point," said the accountant, pointing past Eric's shoulder to some weathered shacks perched on huge gray boulders. The mountains rose in steep gorges behind the rocks. A brook cascaded out of the trees and pooled in a shallow clearing. "The Tlingit Indians used to fish here," Mel explained. "Stretched their nets from here to the Taku Glacier, right across the mouth of this river. Can you believe the guts that must have taken?"

Jerry gazed from Hut Point across more than half a mile of swirling currents to the breast of another glacier.

"Must have been a rough way to make a living."

"Hard but free," Mel commented.

Eric glanced over, smirking. "Yeah, free from what?"

Mel pulled on his brown beard, peered up at him. "The old lady, what else?"

Laughter burst from the two men.

"Why, come next fall," Mel mused, his eyes glinting with humor, "our new buddy, here, will be dying to go hunting. And not because he likes to tramp around in the cold and wet."

"The hell you say," said Jerry.

Mel jabbed his shoulder. "How long you think that lovey-dovey stuff'll last? We saw you two at the boat harbor, hanging on each other like you were going to war or something. Didn't we, McMillan?"

Eric throttled down and peered at the water. "I give 'em one good snowstorm, the cabin isolated the way it is."

"Damn right."

"That's all you know about it," Jerry grinned, hoping Eric's coolness toward him would thaw on this trip. "After putting up with you two jokers for the next few days, being locked up with a woman of quality is the only thing that'll get me sane again."

"You hear that, Eric? He's impugning our honor. 'Woman of quality.' Doesn't it just about turn your stomach, a man in his death throes, struggling through his last free hours on this earth?"

Eric squinted at the water and shook his head in mock disgust. Mel sighed and turned around.

The hell he'd get cabin fever, Jerry thought. He was just about praying for a snowstorm the minute he and Sue Ann got back from Hawaii—his little secret surprise, the plane tickets to Kauai—a good long snowstorm right after the honeymoon was what he was hoping for. It made his stomach drop just thinking about it.

Jerry tugged down his red cap. It did no good; his ears were exposed and numb. And it did no good to wish Sue Ann were with him on this trip; he was on his own. He flipped on the window blade to clear away the rain, and studied the river country.

With dusk closing on them like the cape of Dracula, Eric sent the boat plummeting into a channel of silver-green water near the eastern reach of the Taku Glacier. Half a mile or so upriver, the water swung around a big bend, and the trees, shrouded by drizzle, formed a gray lump in the haze.

On the far shore, a light blinked. Mel said it was the Taku Lodge, still used by sportsmen as a base for hunting and fishing. Gord's Saber Craft sliced the water about a quarter-mile back.

Jerry glanced to his left. The glacier whizzed by like frames in a vintage motion picture, blinking darks and lights. Exhilarated, he chuckled. This *was* the life.

Eric barked, "Hold on!"

Suddenly there was a ripping, tearing sound and a violent shuddering, and the boat jerked to a stop. Jerry's shoulder and forehead rammed into the windshield. Something struck his back. His heart seized, ratcheting through pain, panic, escape. The current, the glacial cold—could he survive?

Mel shoved away from Jerry—he'd thrown a block, evidently, to keep from battering into Jerry.

Eric cursed the river.

"Just like a good woman," Mel scoffed. "Unpredictable. You all right, man?" he asked Jerry.

Amazement washed over him, relief, consternation that he'd been to the very edge of blind panic in seconds, while his companions joked about the near-accident. In the backwash of adrenaline, he realized the hull was intact, the river slurping against it.

"Earth to Jerry," said Mel. "You okay?"

"Fine," he grunted, pulling a bag of provisions off his boot. He sat back. "I'm fine. You?"

"I'm used to it—and damned glad this orange duck can take a beating. Helluva place to learn to swim. How's the tide, Eric?"

Eric didn't answer. Still gripping the wheel, his jaw thrust out, he jabbed a forefinger at the start button. It groaned and didn't turn over the propeller. He poked another switch. The electrics whined and, back at the stern, the motor tilted up out of the water.

"We missed high tide by half an hour," Eric said in a brusque, distracted tone. "Gord said the river was high last weekend, and I thought it would still be flooding. It's lower than I counted on."

"Gord's going like sixty," Mel said, glancing outside.

The other boat hummed in a curve, on-step and tilted to keep them up off the sand. It sailed like a ghostly sphere in the twilight, slipping around them to find a way upriver.

"They might make it," said Eric. "If they find a channel."

Flipping off the motor, Sue Ann's brother ducked aft and dragged an oar from the gunnels. Dipping it into the river, he rocked the hull back and forth. The current lapped against the upstream side.

Across the water, Gord's engine pitched high and stopped. Shouts echoed through the evening.

"They didn't make it," said Mel, crawling out from under the canopy and shielding his eyes from the rain.

Jerry joined the two men, feeling slightly out of his element. He was glad Sue Ann hadn't been here to see him go crashing like a fool into Eric's windshield. Jerking his hat brim low, he studied the water. Evidently the sandbars switched with each storm and tide, so the river couldn't be navigated the same way each time. The bars were like monsters that reached up on a whim to slam into the prow or grab the prop and choke it to a standstill. They were a damned long way from town, Jerry thought grumpily, wondering what they'd do if the next tide didn't lift them off.

He glanced at Eric. He wasn't baby-sitting, that was for sure; he was cutting Jerry no slack, barely being civil. But the man had a lot on his mind.

Eric bent to push the start button on the engine. The prop barely grabbing water, it kicked over, nudged them a few inches. He slid the paddle into the space alongside the tarpaulins and gas cans. With one quick look at the sky, he shook his head. Shouldering around Jerry, his features stretched into a mirthless grin, he said, "Timing is everything, isn't it?"

"No kidding. Anything I can do to help?"

He glanced at Mel. "We ought to let the cheechako wade around in this thirty-degree water, huh?"

Eric picked his way forward. Flipping his Peterbilt cap around backward, making his nose look hawklike, he hunched over to punch buttons.

Mel cuffed Jerry. "Exciting, isn't it? Out here in the wilds with nothing but the bears and seals? Come to think of it, I've never had me a good sleep beside a glacier. You?"

Shaking his head at Mel's humorous machismo and thinking he was damned glad his Remington was under the bow—bears were excellent swimmers—Jerry hiked over the cartons to his seat. He braced a hand against the dash and wedged his boot against the forecastle.

The electric motor whined; the prop lowered into the water. Eric feathered the gears into forward. The steel blades bit into the bar, bogging down and gurgling sand and water into the engine well. But pouring on throttle did no good. The water sloshed at the hull, but the boat didn't even swing around into the current. They were stuck in the muck.

This time Jerry went aft and dug the paddle into the sand. Although he worked several minutes, the murky twilight settled in.

"Might as well give up," said Eric, stepping over boxes.

Stowing the paddle, Jerry sat on a red gas can to unzip his coat. Despite the cold, he had warmed up. His breath puffed in white clouds. He felt better.

Eric stood near the rail and hollered to the other boat, "You guys going to get off the bar?"

"No," came the faint answer.

"Engine okay?"

"Yeah."

"Too dark," he called.

Their running lights came on, and Sam lifted his arm in agreement.

Eric waved and turned to his own crew. "Fifteen years I've been coming up the river, and I've never had to spend the night on the bar. Geez!"

"Happens to the best of us, skipper," Mel said. "I'll get into the boots."

Eric gave him a look just this side of derision. "You can't even swim."

Jerry stepped up. "I can. I'll put the boots on."

Eric's glance was first surprised, then emphatic. "Drop-offs," he said. "You go under in the dark and those boots fill with water, number one, we'll never find you. Number two, you'll last all of ten or fifteen minutes. This water is barely above freezing."

"Somebody's got to—"

"I'll do it. Nothing better to do. Maybe I can get us into enough water to anchor up. We don't want to float around on this river when we're sleeping."

Climbing forward, he flipped on the running lights and the radio. The marine weatherman rattled out the temperature— forty-five degrees—and gave wind and water conditions for various sections of the Southeast. Meanwhile, Eric rummaged in the forecastle and got into the hip boots.

A feeling of brotherhood settled on Jerry. These men knew the country, the dangers, and that didn't stop them from tackling the life-style head on. He admired that.

But, more importantly, they looked out for each other. Eric would no more have left Sam Gord sitting on the docks back in Douglas, bad engine or not, than Jerry would have given up looking for the good life.

The ribbing they gave him was all right, Jerry mused. It was just a test: Are you one of the guys? Can you take a joke? Will you help a man out when he needs it? They might ask him along on their adventures, but they sure as hell weren't going to trust him until he'd earned it. And he didn't blame them. If you were up the river with an idiot or a weakling, it could cost you your life.

FOR FORTY-FIVE MINUTES, Eric sloshed around in the cold water. He pushed the hull this way and that, his shoulders first silhouetted against the glacier and the haze of an eerie night sky, then blended into the darkness on the water as he pussyfooted over the bottom, testing for drop-offs.

Finally out of breath from lugging the stern around, Eric hoisted himself over the stern-wall, grunting like a winded boar. "Might as well get some shut-eye," he said. "We're not going anywhere till first light."

Mel dug under the seats for sleeping bags. He found three and lowered the seats into two padded benches. "Tuck in, ladies. It's going to get cold."

Five minutes later, the plastic flaps at the back of the cab were zipped up, and the cabin was getting warm. Eric lay on the starboard bench, Jerry on the portside, the end of the sleeping bag dangling outside the wind-flaps, getting soaked in the rain.

Eric flipped the toggle switch for the interior lights back and forth, throwing them into the dark, the light, the dark. Jabbing Mel's shoulder, he said, "Lights out, kids. We all comfycozy?"

"Just like bugs in a rug," Mel muttered, rummaging around on the lumpy platform he'd made of boxes and life vests in the aisle. Sighing hard at the unfairness of life, he doubled up a sweater, punched it down and flopped his head on it. "Say g'night, Dick."

"'G'night, Dick,'" Eric mimed, repeating the lines of an old Smothers Brothers routine. The cab went dark. The sleeping bags rustled as the men tried to get comfortable.

Jerry tilted up to peek at the glacier. Five hundred yards away, the ice glowed against black bluffs, reflecting the diffuse light of a moon buried beneath the mist. Reminded of Sue Ann's pale skin, the sheen from lovemaking on her breasts, Jerry felt longing dart through him. But a thud, probably from Mel's foot striking the deck, distracted him.

Mel cursed.

"You want my coat?" Jerry asked. "It's damp, but I don't need it in this down bag. It's under the bow."

"Hell, no, Teal. I want my heated waterbed and Brenda in it, that's what I want."

"But just think," Jerry joshed, "isn't this exciting, camping out with the bears and seals? Right beside a glacier?"

Eric snorted.

Mel growled.

Jerry lay back, grinning, feeling good. He turned to Eric, barely able to see the line of his shoulder. "How's the mine survey coming along, anyway?"

"Couldn't be better," Eric said. "Contract signed, crew out on the mountain, ecology guys all angry because we're handling the wilderness with kid gloves."

"The environmentalists pretty powerful up here?"

"You bet. They love to bust a crew. I gave word I wanted every man on this job to consider he's walking on eggshells. I can't afford any stupid mistakes."

"I should be so smart," Mel complained. "I should have stayed home."

"Aw, shut up and go to sleep," Eric said. "The way you snore, in five minutes you won't even know what you're sleeping on. You'll rattle yourself right up off your bedroll, like one of those levitators." The nylon swished as Eric turned completely over. "I hope to God you put the eggs in the bottom of those boxes when you packed them, Teal. I like 'em lookin' at me, not scrambled."

"G'night, Dick," said Jerry.

Wiggling his toes to warm them, Jerry closed his eyes. He didn't have a permit to shoot a moose, because he'd come up too late to apply for one. That was okay; if they made a kill, it was customary to share. To give him a purpose, the guys had made him the cook for this trip, and Jerry had been on enough hunting and fishing expeditions to know the value men put on a good cook out in the wilderness. He'd supervised the grocery shopping, packed the boxes of food for both boats. Nobody had said thanks, but he could wait. Among his Los Angeles buddies, he was famous for his biscuits and gravy.

Rocked by the river, Jerry drifted to sleep thinking that even Sue Ann didn't realize he was a "mean machine" around a camp stove. But then, there were lots of things she didn't know about him yet.

SOMEBODY MUST HAVE kicked his bunk. Jerry lurched awake to see the bulkhead tilted at a weird angle. He looked outside. Dawn filtered pale light across the bow. It was nippy, but the sky was beginning to yellow in the east, promising a clear day. Jerry had to angle his head to see a level line of trees on either shore. He pulled himself up, and what he saw made his jaw slacken in amazement. They'd drifted downriver. They were in the middle of the river, about half a mile below the Taku Lodge, and all around the boat was sand, nothing but sandbar. They were keeled over on it. Marooned.

They shared the bar with a huge log blackened by moisture, its jagged end pointing upstream. Another ten yards closer, Jerry thought, and he didn't want to imagine what that lighting spur would have done to a fast-drifting hull. No wonder Eric was out on deck, scowling.

Mel was struggling to sit up. He and the boxes were crammed up against the skipper's bench. Dragging a squished bag of marshmallows off his lap, Mel flung them at Jerry. Jerry ducked and laughed.

Pulling his legs out of the snarl of nylon and down, Jerry hauled the sleeping bag inside. The end was wet; it smelled like moldy carrot greens. Stuffing it under the bow, with the wet end draped on the seat to air out, he shouldered into the all-weather coat. Then he forced his cramped legs to life and scooted outside.

Onshore, an eagle soared along the tops of the cedars and cottonwoods. He heard crows cawing in the woods. Two seals drifted past the bar, their flat brown heads and spaniels' eyes swiveling to watch the men.

Jerry scooped in a deep breath. The air was scented with pine and leaf mold. Cold, wild. It made him feel cocky.

Across the deck, which lay at thirty degrees, Eric was looking mournfully at the sandbar. Jerry waved at it. "Nice place to visit, but I wouldn't want to put my house on it," he said.

The comment nudged a smile out of Eric. "Teal, you're a barrel of laughs."

"When the chips are down, a little laugh never hurts," said Mel, burrowing out on deck. Down feathers curled in his beard and hair. Leaning against the uphill rail, he scrubbed his scalp and watched white wisps float away. Then he said to Eric, "Where's Sam?"

Eric scouted upstream. "Maybe they went up to the cabin to get the riverboat." He glanced at Jerry. "It's got a jet prop. Skims over the bars like a bird. We can offload the gear and maybe float away from this damned desert we're on. It'd be nice to get in at least a couple hours of hunting."

Jerry frowned. "We should have heard them if they started up the engine. Sound really carries here."

Eric looked downstream, nodding agreement, his eyes thoughtful. "I wish to God Sam Gord would get a radio for his boat. Well," he said, "we might as well relax. We're not going anywhere till the noon tide."

"If then," said Mel. "We managed to drift onto the biggest damned bar I've ever seen in this river, and I'm starving to death."

Eric glanced at Jerry. "Remind me to bring a muzzle, next time."

They climbed over the downside rail and walked around on the sand and gravel. It squished underfoot. An hour passed, and the river began to creep up the bar, but not by much. They were still yards from the water—hours from a hot breakfast and a hike up Fish Creek to the moose.

The men sat on the damp log, pitching pebbles. Stomachs growling, they griped that all Jerry had brought were steaks and shrimp and other gourmet delights that had to be cooked. At last they toyed with the idea of eating marshmallow-and-peanut butter sandwiches.

"We could wash it down with beer," said Eric, pulling out his pipe.

Mel stared at the pipe and frowned. "What do you do with that thing?" he said. "Put it down the garbage disposal once a week?"

"Teeth marks give it character," said Eric, giving the stem an affectionate look before clamping it in his mouth. He grinned around it.

Mel shook his head in disgust and tossed a pebble.

Eric flicked his Bic, touching it to the bowl, sucking on the bit till smoke rose from the tobacco.

Suddenly Jerry glanced from the flame to the log and stood up. "Borrow that," he said, holding out his hand.

Eric gave him the lighter—and a gaze that said Jerry might be going off the deep end and ought to be watched.

"Where's your motor oil?" Jerry asked.

"Back of the boat. Half a case. Why?"

"Feel like a hot breakfast?"

"Sure, but—"

Mel stood. "Definitely." He glanced at Eric, at Jerry. "What have you got up your sleeve, Teal?"

"Sudden inspiration. Bacon and eggs coming up."

"But we don't have a cook stove on board," said Eric, jabbing his pipe at the bar. "And no kindling to start a fire . . ."

Jerry walked away, laughing. *Teal*, he thought, *sometimes you're a genius.*

Half an hour later, he'd whittled a shallow depression in the trunk of the driftwood log and poured in some gas and motor

oil. He lit the mixture and let the worst of the smoke burn off.
Emptying three cans of beer, he filled two of them with eggs
and river water and the third with half a pound of bacon. He
set the cans on the flame. They began to sizzle and send off
delicious odors.

Glancing in amusement at the openmouthed stares of his
companions, he said with mock servility, "Gentlemen, will it
be coffee or beer with breakfast?"

"Coffee," said Mel and Eric, punching each other and
hooting like six-year-olds.

Jerry sacrificed two more cans of beer. They could share the
two coffees. Beer was too precious to hunters to go hog-wild
wasting it. He sprinkled some grounds into the empty cans,
added water, and set them to boil.

The nutty scent of the brew reminded him of Sue Ann, the
first few minutes they'd made love, because the coffee maker
had been on then, the smell mingling with the wisps of wood
smoke, and he'd seen the image of New Hampshire bluebells
in her eyes.

He narrowed his gaze upstream, remembering. The sun
touched the rim of the glacier, turning it ice-blue; and the rays
shone through the trees at the bend in the river, reminding him
of a postcard he'd kept as a kid, kept so long the enamel finish wore away and the sky turned cardboard-gray. Finally he'd
lost it somewhere. He'd missed that postcard, thought about
it for years. Even when he'd been stationed in the Aleutian Islands, and had left the bleak islands to go hunting on the
mainland, he'd always watched for a scene that looked like his
old postcard. Now he'd found it. The Taku River on a clear,
cold morning could take your breath away; it could make you
realize you just had to keep looking till you found what you
wanted in life.

The sunlight gleamed on the water and on the pocketknives
the men were using to jab at the eggs, and Jerry knew a profound satisfaction.

When he turned back to eat his breakfast, Eric was staring
at him. The skipper chuckled, his eyes alight. "You're all right,
Teal," he said. "You'll do."

Jerry scraped an egg out of the can, popped it into his
mouth and chewed. It was probably the best egg he'd ever

tasted. He grinned and looked at Eric. "Will I do well enough for you to get yourself over to the chapel on Saturday? It'd mean a lot to Sue Ann."

Eric slammed the can of coffee onto the log and put his hands on his knees, his eyes flaring. "Well, who the hell do you think's going to give her away, Teal? Santy Claus?"

Chapter Ten

"They're here," Laura said.

Sue Ann laughed with excitement. "Twenty minutes, I'll be there just as soon as I can get over the bridge, Laura."

"Missed him, huh?"

She let out a little whoop of enthusiasm that earned her a double take from Zelda, the brunette at the cash register in the store where she was buying her wedding shoes. "Like crazy. I missed him like crazy."

"Geez, girl, get ahold of yourself. It's not like he's been gone a month. You're going to wear the poor man down."

Sue Ann giggled. "You don't know Jerry. See you at the boat harbor, Laura. I'll be the one with the big grin on my face."

They were all milling around the loading ramp when she drove down Savikko Road to the Douglas Boat Harbor: the men with stubbled faces, already hooking the second boat to a trailer behind Gord's white pickup; the women in jeans and jackets, their faces wearing a tad more makeup than usual and their hair brushed to a gleam. Sue Ann had been around this scene for years, yet this was the first time she could remember feeling as if she were sixteen. She checked her own makeup. The lavender eye shadow, blended into a darker shade above her lids, matched the sweater she wore beneath her jacket and the ribbon tied in a bow around her ponytail. Her best cords and her kid leather town boots slimmed her legs. And then she realized how silly she was being. The men would be grubby from hunting, and in half an hour she and Laura would be up to their elbows in the messy business of packaging the moose meat. She shook her head and climbed out of the Subaru.

Laura, too, had invested a few extra minutes in grooming. As she stood by the dented green pickup, her brown blunt-cut hair swung in the breeze and shone like a beaver pelt. Her short, rounded figure looked its best in a blue Woolrich rain jacket and jeans.

She gave me a bad time about being excited, Sue Ann thought, but ten years hadn't exactly dulled the shine on her own marriage.

Jerry, Eric and Mel were laughing with Laura. A spear of exhilaration went through Sue Ann as she approached them. There was a closeness about the three men, a natural camaraderie that was not induced by alcohol; the relaxed boyishness told her Jerry was one of them. At last. Now, if only Eric would help mend the fences . . .

"Hey, don't tell all your war stories," she called, kicking gravel in her rush to get down the ramp. "Save me some."

Jerry turned, one hand tucked into the back pocket of his jeans. His unshaven face broke into a grin. "There she is!"

Mel said something about, "Oh, geez, the lovebirds again."

Jerry hurried to her, scooped her in his arms, and now she couldn't hear Mel or the sea gulls or the thud of equipment down on the docks, because Jerry was saying her name—"Sue Ann, honey" —and kissing her as if he'd been gone a month.

"Eric's giving you away," he said against her ear, softly and with laughter in his voice.

She gave him a look of incredulity. "You're kidding?"

"He got all riled up when I even suggested he might not. Said who did I think was going to give you away, Santy Claus?"

They hooted and danced around, and Sue Ann tore out of his arms and ran to Eric and hugged him.

"What the hell?" Eric staggered back, blushing.

"Oh, Eric, you'll do it? Give me away?"

"If I last that long. Lord, Sue Ann, you just about busted my lip, running into me that way. You lost your sense of direction or something?"

Everyone howled with laughter because all of them had been waiting, as she had, for old Scrooge's heart to melt.

BLOOD TESTS and applying for the marriage license and final
fittings and consultations and errands filled the whole week
before the wedding, and Sue Ann was as much buoyed by it as
Jerry was dazed.

"Appointment with the dressmaker—check," she read from
her list, while Jerry read the *Post-Intelligencer* he'd gotten
from the waitress. They were lunching at the Breakwater on
Thursday, at a front table overlooking the boat harbor and the
bridge to Douglas. "Tuxedo fitting—you and Eric did that,
right, babe?" She glanced up, saw him engrossed, and continued, "Yes, that's right, you told me last night it was done.

"Photographer—check. Caterer's final-final—check."

"Is 'honeymoon' on the list?" he asked, folding the paper
and laying it by his water glass.

She smiled, feeling tender. "No, of course not, hon. We'll
tuck into the cabin and put a message on the recorder that says
'Gone fishing for days and days.' Something like that."

"I have a hankering to go south after the wedding. How
about you?"

Sue Ann's heart lurched. "South? To L.A.?"

"No, no. Don't look so panic-stricken. I've had enough of
that city to last a lifetime. I meant . . . someplace warm and is-
landy. You know, romantic. Palm trees, sand, exotic music."

"But we've got exotic music at the cabin." She looked at a
sprig of parsley that had fallen to the table when the plates
were cleared, feeling an inexplicable disappointment that Jerry
would even suggest they not honeymoon at the cabin. Perhaps, she told herself, glancing at him, he was just being
thoughtful, trying to find out what she wanted. "You haven't
begun to see the music I've collected over the years, Jerry," she
said, her voice earnest. "It would take you months to hear it
all. And we've got the warm waterbed, and the woods and
beaches to explore, and I've stocked the kitchen with incredible goodies. Oh, it'll be wonderful, the two of us, getting to
know each other at the cabin."

"It's what you want?"

"Oh, yes. It's been in my mind all year."

His face looked peculiar. She couldn't quite read it, as if he
were struggling with a problem. "What is it, Jerry? You do
love the cabin—find it peaceful, comfortable?"

"Well, I do, but—" he was stumbling, too, and she felt a strange tension between them, even as he recovered "—but I thought you were looking forward to traveling, too. We talked about seeing Venice, England, Hawaii. If it's the money, sweetheart, don't ever worry about that. My treat."

"The money won't be a problem," she said, and then broke off. Jerry couldn't know her inheritance would come to her Saturday. Saturday, if it were coming from someone such as her aunt, who would attend the wedding, she mused; or Monday, surely, if the mysterious donor were to wire it, say, after learning about the wedding in the newspaper. What a great relief it would be to have the secret revealed and explained to everyone, especially Jerry. The weight of her secret felt too unwieldy for their new relationship. Meeting his gaze and seeing his quizzical expression, she realized she'd left off with an awkward pause. "That is," she said, "it isn't money I was thinking of."

"What are you thinking?"

"That we have years ahead of us to travel, darling." She reached for his hand, squeezed his fingers. "I'll want to see everything with you, Jerry," she said. "But our honeymoon—I think we ought to keep things simple, don't you? Get to know each other and your new home before we traipse off to the far corners of the earth?"

He shrugged without answering, but looked almost convinced.

She felt, absurdly, that she must sell him on the idea of staying home at all costs. "And, you know me, babe," she said, rubbing his hand. "I'd have to check out the options on hotels, car rentals, air fares. I'd want to make sure there were no revolutions going on in the country we wanted to visit. I'd be in a dither if the baggage got lost or the reservation got loused up. Details, details. It would all have to be arranged."

"What if I did the arranging?"

"But I've said I don't mind handling such things, and you detest it. Why put yourself out when there's no need?"

"Then, of course, we'll stay home this time."

"You're sure you don't mind? It's your honeymoon, too."

"I'll make it worth my while, don't worry about that."

Affection warmed his face again. They smiled, the promise of sensuous pleasure connecting them so that they rose from the table at the same moment, without words.

"You've got your details to manage today and tomorrow," he said, walking her to the car, "and I promised to meet Sam Gord after he gets off work."

"What are the two of you up to?"

"Boatyard-hopping. He wants a rebuilt motor for his boat and I said I'd go with him."

"Aren't you the typical Alaskan male, running off to hunt and mess with boats."

"And don't you love it, too," he said, giving her a jaunty chuck under the chin. "You've got your good-ol'-boy husband and I've got my sourdough wife—day after tomorrow. Won't we be the happy couple, my love?"

And he put her into the car, kissed her nose, shut the door and walked off whistling.

To GET AN EARLY START the next morning, she slept in the loft at Eric and Laura's. When she rose, dressed in blue slacks and a sweater, and came downstairs to have fruit and coffee, the weatherman just about made her cry. He announced another storm. Sue Ann looked across Gastineau Channel to see a familiar gunmetal tint to the overcast skies.

"Laura," she said to her sister-in-law, who looked over from dusting the gun cabinet. "Aunt Ester and the others might have a devil of a time getting in this afternoon. It's supposed to snow."

"Not to worry. Eric said he thought the flights today would be okay. Just be glad you set the time for the wedding early, so everybody from Seattle and L.A. had to get in today."

"But there's still the ring," Sue Ann said, wrapping a blue scarf inside the collar of her jacket and collecting her purse from the couch. "My friend in Phoenix said he was sending an associate with it. Mickey Stone. What if he doesn't arrive?"

"I think that's an abominable name for a man in the gem trade," said Laura, locking the gun case and stretching to ease her back. To cool off, she plucked at her faded red T-shirt, stretching the word Louie's into unintelligible black lines, and said, "What if Jerry's last name were 'Ledger?' Or Eric's 'Survey?' "

"Mmm," murmured Sue Ann, preoccupied with the possibility Mickey Stone wouldn't arrive with Jerry's wedding ring. She knew it was just a symbol. The ring stood for respectability, safety, fidelity—the things she'd lost in the affair with Mark. It bothered her that the ring might not arrive in time for the wedding. She wanted Jerry to have the most stunning symbol of happiness anyone in Juneau had ever seen. Besides, they certainly couldn't have a wedding without a ring for the groom. It was unthinkable.

"I once knew a family named Trout," Laura chatted, dusting an end table. "I went to school with Lake, poor boy. One of his sisters was saddled with Rainbow, can you imagine? They went on the Merv Griffin show."

There was a lull in the conversation. "What if Serena can't get to the airport because it's flooding in Seattle?" said Sue Ann.

"Now, look." Tossing her oil rag to the table, Laura came to her and grasped her arm. "Jerry's picking up his business partner at noon, and everyone else will be in at four. Relax. You've just got the premarital jitters. Everything will be fine."

"It's all coming so fast."

"And you've planned it like a field general. Now stop this." Laura tucked the scarf in close to Sue Ann's throat. "You're marrying the man of your dreams. Be happy."

"That's what Viv said yesterday when I went in for my pamper session."

Laura smiled wistfully. "Someday I'm going to have everything done—nails, facial, pedicure. It must be the absolute height of luxury."

Sue Ann tried to bank her doubts; she looked affectionately at her cute, sturdy sister-in-law. Gently she smoothed the shining brown hair. "Here I am rattling on about the weather and airplanes, and you've got the world on your shoulders." She hugged Laura. "The mine contract will change everything," she whispered. "You'll even be able to vacation in Jamaica, you'll see."

They held each other, close and comfortable with the years of steady friendship behind them. Then Laura pushed away, looking firmly into Sue Ann's eyes. "And you," she said, "had better get moving. Your friends at Fisheries won't wait that party till the afternoon break, if I know the rules around a government office. Get a move on. I'll meet you at the airport at four. All the relatives will be there, and so will Mickey Rock."

"Stone."

"All right, Stone. He'll be there with the ring. Now get moving. I've got to get this house in some kind of shape before Aunt Ester arrives, or she'll threaten to cut Eric out of her will for having a slothful wife. She'd mean well, but I have my pride."

Literally pushed out the door, Sue Ann conducted her round of errands and arrived at the airport on time.

If the crowds were distracting, it was also wonderful to feel the family surrounding her like a pack of affectionate puppies—cousins, aunts, uncles, some of them with the dark hair and chiseled features of Sue Ann's mother; others with the Irish red hair and freckles of the McMillans. Aunt Ester, with her twinkling blue eyes and her tailored burgundy suit from Saks, shook a finger at her and demanded Sue Ann be happy for the rest of her life.

"Oh, I will," she said, looking past her aunt's slim shoulders. "Where's my little girl?" she said. "I don't see Serena."

"Where you'd expect," said Ester. "Entertaining a whole crew of backpackers in the rear of the plane. Smoking section, Sue Ann. I scolded her, dear, but of course, you can't tell children anything."

"Smoking? Serena? She hates smoke."

"Do you mean when she was a gawky ten-year-old and had some sense? That was ten years ago. Evidently she thinks she's grown-up now."

"But where is she? I don't see—"

And finally, laughing and chatting with two husky men who looked as if they'd just come off the Chilkoot Pass, Serena came striding up the debarkation ramp.

Oh, she looks beautiful, thought Sue Ann, her eyes filling. She watched Serena toss her mane of wavy black hair and send that piercing blue-eyed gaze through the crowd in the waiting room. She wore a billowy jacket of pale blue, a wide black scarf with the hem of blue-and-magenta swirls tossed over her shoulder. Such elan—but she's too slim, thought Sue Ann, aching to get her arms around her daughter. Serena's concerned gaze and the black slacks fitted into leather ankle boots gave her the look of a ski instructor studying the slopes for wayward students. She had that look; a fiery presence, a sharp awareness, and a gaze of compassion.

The love welled up in Sue Ann, and she called her daughter, and ran to wrap her in a warm embrace.

"Mama, you've lost weight," Serena murmured, her voice choked with excitement and emotion as she hung on with the old expressiveness Sue Ann adored. "You look sixteen," she added. "I've missed you so much, Mama."

"Me too, baby. You're far too thin, but I suppose it's the pressure of your last year at school. How are you, really, darling?"

They broke apart. "Fine. I know I'll be asked to join a fabulous design firm. But I'm dying to meet Jerry." She sent that lightning-bolt gaze through the knot of relatives watching their reunion. "Where is he?"

"With Clint, his business partner. He left us this time to ourselves. You, me, the family."

"Oh." Disappointment tinged her voice.

"He's thoughtful that way," Sue Ann said, smoothing a wild lock of Serena's hair. "He knew I'd want to know all about school and your social life and your plans."

"There're tons of things to tell," she said, catching Laura's eye and beaming. "Hi, Aunt Laura. Oh, look at Tana! She's so big. Hi, sweetie, do you remember your Aunt Serena and that baseball we found at the boat harbor last Easter?"

Tana came forward, nodding, smiling shyly, and Serena hustled the child up into her arms to tease away a kiss.

And the family converged, hugging and laughing, a nucleus of such energy the other passengers stepped out of the way to let them get downstairs to the baggage.

That night, the men took Jerry into the nightlife of downtown Juneau for the mysterious rite of the bachelor party, while Sue Ann, Viv, Laura and a few other close friends, aunts and cousins gathered at a kind of bachelorette's reception at Mike's Place in Douglas.

Built into a hill at the edge of Gastineau Channel, the restaurant had boxy stucco lines. Below the stairs that led from the street-level lobby, the dinner tables were packed with patrons enjoying the superb steak and shrimp louis entrées for which Mike's Place was noted. A band played sixties oldies from the corner of the bar at the back. Candles flickered soft lights against the wood paneling and the faces of the diners.

Tomorrow Sue Ann's wedding guests would be dancing and visiting and sampling the delicacies of the buffet tables, the crab and salmon salads, the teriyaki chicken, the smoked salmon; the entire restaurant would be filled with people congratulating her and Jerry, toasting their happiness.

It all seemed as dreamlike to her as the white veil dancing in the darkness beyond the windows. Ordinarily the tables at the west end of the dining room, where her family and friends were gathered, would be backed by a spectacular view of the lights of Juneau. Now the snow slanted and swirled around the porch rails. Sue Ann felt a little like that view—the emotions blinking and beckoning through a shroud of cool composure.

The most anchoring fact of the evening was Serena. Poised, warm and confident, her daughter wandered among the tables, her arm linked in Sue Ann's, laughter breaking from her as she listened to family legends and the latest gossip about her hometown. Serena had great prospects for happiness, Sue Ann thought, allowing herself a moment of pride for her dedication in raising her child. Yet it was poignant to realize that this polished, self-contained young woman no longer needed constant nurturing. It made Sue Ann feel sad, made her want the marriage with Jerry even more, to fill the void.

The two of them eventually found a moment to slip upstairs to the lobby, where they could talk in private. A lingering sense of parental responsibility urged Sue Ann to chastise Serena for taking up the habit of smoking. "I was disappointed to find out," Sue Ann said. "You know the statistics."

Serena looked down at her hands, pulling at her university ring. "Mama," she said, "I'm a big girl now." She looked into Sue Ann's eyes. "Don't worry about me anymore. Go for what makes *you* happy."

Sue Ann's heart contracted. "I'm still your mother. I care so much, darling."

"I know. I'm not overdoing anything. Trust me."

"I do already. I'm so lucky to have had you." Sue Ann caressed her hair, remembering ... as a two-year-old Serena lay sleeping in the battered orange station wagon, midnight curls hugging her temples, oblivious of the tough decision Sue Ann had made to rescue the bear cub. Both of them, Serena and the cub, had survived all these years and emerged strong. Sue Ann shook her head at the miracle of it. "The time has flown by," she said, smiling. "You're so ... complete, Serena. So perfect."

"Chip off the old block," she laughed. Then she leaned forward, hugged Sue Ann and stood back to look at her. "It was hard to raise a kid by yourself, but you did it. For me. Now I know I can do the hard things in life, too. Because you're my mom."

Sue Ann's throat closed and she drew a breath.

Serena rescued her, touched her arm. "Aunt Laura said you were panic-stricken because Jerry's ring didn't arrive today. Where is it?"

"Stone, the gem man, has been delayed. If the snow lets up, he'll arrive tomorrow." She frowned. "He may miss the wedding."

Twisting off her school ring, Serena held it out. The band was gold, the stone topaz because, like Sue Ann, Serena was a November child. "Something borrowed," said her daughter. "You've got to borrow something for luck. Will this fit Jerry's pinkie finger, do you think?"

Suddenly the tears would not be checked. Sue Ann was crying, and Serena held her, hushing her. "Mama, it'll be okay," she crooned. "Just the pressure. I always cry at finals. It's nothing. You feel as if you won't be able to make it, but you can. You're so strong, Mama. It always pulls me through, remembering how strong you are."

"I know, Serena, but sometimes I feel so—" She choked back feelings of uncertainty.

"Nonsense," said her grown child, sounding very like Ester, but displaying her own brand of uncanny intuition. "You've got the jitters. You think you'll be cut off from the world by getting married. No way, Mama. Your family will always be there if you need us."

"Baby, I know. But Jerry's ring. It was his wedding gift, his surprise. It was so important I give him this ring to let him know we'll build something permanent, something lasting."

Serena held her away, her eyes perplexed. "But a ring can't prove that, Mama."

Sue Ann wiped her eyes. "What do you mean?"

"It's people that count. Not things. A ring is just a ring, Mama."

"It's a symbol," she insisted, not wanting to tell her daughter it was all she might be able to give Jerry now—a symbol that she trusted him to face the dragons of life with her.

Serena peered anxiously into her face. "He's still as jolly and lovable as you told me, that time last summer when you called about the wedding? You will be happy?"

In those intelligent blue eyes that missed nothing of the world around her, Sue Ann recognized concern. She had never lied to Serena, and the subject of marriage was no place to start. She would be gently honest.

"There are no guarantees, my love," she said softly. "All any couple can do is try to trust each other and prove their respect."

"But is he worth it? Will he hurt you?"

"Not intentionally, darling. He's a good man. Jolly and lovable and tender and world-traveled—all the things I said he was." Feeling surer of herself, she smiled. "It's the pressure, that's all. I feel much better." She took the class ring, hugged it to her chest. "Thank you for this ring. Jerry and I will be happy, you'll see."

Serena nodded.

Sue Ann saw the lingering doubt, and said with more passion, "Never stop believing love and happiness are possible, sweetheart. They are."

"Okay." Serena gave her a brilliant smile. "Jerry sounds perfect for you, Mama. Go for the gusto."

THE NEXT MORNING, the Taku Wind blew somewhere to the south of Juneau. Snow fell in earnest now, and on the outskirts of town, the giant flakes blanketed the shore of a bay and the spit of land leading out to a stone chapel set amid huge evergreens. Several guests walked among the weathered stations of the cross scattered through the woods, gazed at the storm-shrouded bay, before entering the church.

A hubbub of voices filtered through the door of the tiny dressing room off the chancery, reminding Sue Ann of the soft timbre of Jerry's voice. Viv fussed with the flowers in her hair, and Sue Ann smoothed the jacket of her velvet suit. Would Jerry like it? The outfit was a deep rose shade, snug around the torso, the skirt fluted to fall gracefully around her calves. He'd like it, she decided. He seemed to like everything about her. As Laura retied the bow at the back of Tana's pink dress, and Serena went to usher the photographer into the chapel, Sue Ann thought back over the telephone conversation she'd had with Jerry earlier that morning.

"How're you feeling?" he'd asked, the warmth coming through the line, instantly connecting them.

"As if I needed another two weeks," she'd chuckled, effectively hiding her nervousness. "How was the bachelor party?"

"Oh, great. They took me to that cancan-dancers show. Needless to say, all those gorgeous legs reminded me of you."

"I'll bet," she scoffed.

"No, really. More fuel hardly needed to be added to the fire, if you know what I mean. Lord, I miss you, sourdough. If the wedding were in two weeks instead of this morning, I swear I'd abduct you tonight."

She felt the thrill of his longing clear into her fingertips. "Don't change your plans."

"You're right," he said, low and sexy. "At about three o'clock this afternoon, be ready."

"Or what?" she said, a little breathless.

"Or I'll throw you over my shoulder and carry you from the safety of your family. And you'll know the reason why."

"Just to show off?"

He laughed. "You wish."

"Oh, Jerry."

"'Oh, Jerry,'" he mimicked. "I want to hear that tonight, Sue Ann. Your legs wrapped around me and that sweet moan in your voice—oh, Jerry—like you'll die if I don't love you till daybreak. You 'Oh, Jerry' me now and I'll come straight to the cabin, forget the wedding.''

"Oh, Jerry," she said with a lusty bead in her voice—and then she giggled. "Remind me to thank the cancan girls next time I'm in town."

"I told you, it wasn't them."

"Uh-huh . . ."

He laughed again. "They were pretty sexy."

"That's what I thought."

"And I think you're pretty sexy. I'll show you what I mean when we get home tonight. For now, I just called to tell you I'll be right there by your side all day. Weddings can get chaotic. Let's stay in touch."

Thinking how thoughtful he'd been to let her know so inconspicuously that he understood her fear of crowds, she'd hung up after talking to him and rushed through the last minute details at the cabin—chilling the champagne, stacking more wood, setting out the rose china they'd use for the first time as husband and wife. She sent Serena pounding up the stairs in search of the college ring. When she came down, Sue Ann tossed her the car keys. "You drive, Serena," she said. "I can't concentrate."

After hastily banking the coals in the potbellied stove so the fire would be easy to start when she and Jerry arrived home, she and Serena slammed out of the cabin at a run.

Home, she thought, listening to the wedding guests in the chapel while Viv added the last lily of the valley to a mass of curls cascading from her crown to her shoulder. He'd called the cabin home. He would love it as she did, and they would be happy. *Please, God.*

"Please," said a child's voice.

Sue Ann glanced down. Tana's strawberry-red curls gleamed, and her eyes shone with excitement. She fluffed the lace on her bodice. "Can I keep this dress after the wedding, please, Aunt Sue? It fits me just right. I can wear it to Rachael's birthday party."

"Of course, sweetheart. It'll never fit me."

"I know," Tana giggled. "You're a grown-up. I still think you look like Lady Di, except she wore white at her wedding, and Daddy says that means—"

"Never mind what Daddy says," interrupted Laura, giving her daughter's dress a tug, then rolling her eyes at Sue Ann and Viv.

Viv smiled, a hint of the indulgent grandmother in her expression. She looked far from the classic grandmotherly type, however. She wore a wide-shouldered fitted suit of royal blue, as daring a wedding color as Sue Ann's own magenta dress. Next to the blue, Viv's skin looked like porcelain and her hair like new pennies.

Viv patted Sue Ann's shoulder. "Thunderation," she said with regret. "It doesn't look as if Stone's going to make it."

Sue Ann glanced through a tiny window. Rivulets of spruce bark rose out of sight—the trees were visible from the narrow windows in the vaulted chapel, too; like sentinels, she thought, using every ploy she knew to keep her emotions in check. A patch of sky hovered dark and low over the branches, and snow, already six inches deep, drifted onto the slope. The snowplows would be laboring to keep the roads cleared. She and Jerry would have to be careful driving home, especially if it turned cold and froze the slush. Mickey Stone was a glitch, because of the snow. She'd left word for him at the airport, but his absence nagged her—a detail left dangling.

"I know you're right about Stone, Viv," said Sue Ann, reluctantly turning back to her friend. "I'm so disappointed."

"It's a barrel of pickles, girl. But at least you have the other ring. Forget Stone." Viv consulted her watch. "Curtain time. I'd better check with Clint again, see if everybody's seated and ready for the show."

Sue Ann smiled, thinking of the grave dignified man who was Jerry's business partner.

If she didn't know better, she'd think Viv was smitten, the way she was inspecting her makeup in the mirror. Clint had already agreed to come directly to the dressing room to let Sue Ann know when Mickey Stone arrived with the ring. He hadn't come, and Viv had been out twice to see him about it.

"It wouldn't hurt to check with Clint one more time, I suppose," Sue Ann said, coming to peer over Viv's shoulder. "Then all you have to do is gaze adoringly at him and try not to stumble when you take your seat."

Pink raced up Viv's cheeks. "Don't be silly," she said, again checking her watch. "I don't gaze adoringly at any man." She ducked out of the way to speak to Laura. "You ready, sweetie? I'm burning up in here. I hope the chapel's cool."

Laura picked up a small bouquet of rosebuds from a table, handed a basket of flowers to Tana, took her daughter's free hand and said, "All set." To Sue Ann, "We'll go get Eric. Do I have it right, now? Tana will go first with the ring. Me next, followed by Serena, then you and Eric."

Sue Ann nodded, feeling the pressure begin to knot her stomach. She looked a little desperately at Vivian.

Her friend tucked a loose flower into Sue Ann's coiffure and smiled. "You're a stunner, sweetie. You'll knock his socks off."

"Oh, Viv." Sue Ann hugged her. "Thanks for everything." She gathered Laura close. "You, too. You and Viv and Serena have been priceless. No bride ever had better attendants."

Looking glassy-eyed with emotion, Laura led Tana out. At the door, Viv glanced over her shoulder and gave Sue Ann the victory sign, then disappeared—as dignified a woman as Clint Moss would ever want to meet, and a woman whose earthy humor would put a grin on the lips of the dourest, most homesick soldier overseas. But the victory sign brought a lump to Sue Ann's throat, not a smile.

Alone in the small room, she listened to the ethereal notes of the soprano vocalist, and felt...lonely? What was this feeling that swept her? Fear of failure? She had forsaken her busy life and loving family and friends to make a life with one man. A man who said he wanted years with her, and in the next breath, said he'd try to be there when she needed him.

Try, Jerry? she wanted to shout through the walls.

Trembling, she went to the casement. The snow fell and fell. Endless white. Endless...loneliness. Lonely if she ran from love, lonely if she fell in love and lost him. *Jerry, I want to love you but I'm frightened. Will you know it when I come to you? Will it shatter your confidence in me?*

The door creaked. Clearing her throat, arranging her features, she turned. Serena hurried into the room.

"Everyone's seated," her daughter announced, her eyes alight and appraising Sue Ann. "Mama, you're beautiful."

Sue Ann's lips trembled. She was losing the edges of her control. Going to the table, picking up her bridal bouquet, she said in a bright, brittle voice, "How does he look?"

"Jerry? Handsome. As we agreed last night after I met him, he does look like Harrison Ford. Maybe a little older, with darker hair."

"But don't you love his face? The crow's-feet, his look of intelligence, that nice track down either side of his mouth?" She plucked at a pink rosebud. "I wish Stone had gotten here."

"He will, I'm sure of it. He'll be at the reception."

"Does he look fabulous in white?"

"Mama." She came to Sue Ann and kissed her cheek. "You're wound up. I guess I would be, too." She turned Sue Ann gently toward the door. "Eric's outside. Be happy, Mama."

She was saying "I will," and suddenly the moments blended in a whirl of music and movement, and Eric led her to Jerry, who took her hand and brought her next to him. Jerry, in white. Like the snow, like the isolation she'd felt moments ago...

Sue Ann stood beside him, cold and unconnected. Her skin burned at his sudden, gentle touch, as if she'd been frostbitten, then thawed by the potbellied stove. He was trying to reach her, but she stared at Reverend Walker's hooked nose and thin lips, words about devotion and trust floating over her like veils.

Reverend Walker—officiating in this chapel by permission of the Catholic church, though he was a Protestant minister—raised his thin arms. He encompassed the church, the spartan pews, the white walls, the Gothic windows set deep in stone. The church had always appealed to Sue Ann because it seemed to symbolize the Alaskan's attempt to keep the wilderness at bay. Yet sometimes the wilderness was within.

"Our Father, Who art in Heaven," she prayed with the congregation. Her voice faltered; her devotion felt small, and Sue Ann prayed harder, for faith. The lyrics of "Ave Maria" swept over her and died away. Silence descended. The snow seemed to thunder down to earth.

Eric cleared his throat—emotion gripped him, Sue Ann knew, wishing her sense of unreality had blown away with the Taku Wind, so she could feel bolstered by Eric's love and Jerry's hope.

A dress rustled. She saw Tana's delicate face, grave and sweet—years away from the pain of life and loving, Sue Ann thought vaguely; years away from losing those who would tear out her heart with their going. Her niece handed the college ring to Clint Moss, who wore the gray tuxedo with the wine-red cummerbund that matched his rose boutonniere. Clint bowed slightly, winked at Tana, and handed the ring to Reverend Walker. The minister blessed it; gold and topaz gleamed in the wintry light.

Tana stepped back into place between Laura and her cousin.

Serena stared at Sue Ann with round, lightning-blue eyes. Sue Ann's heart lurched. How could she teach her daughter to trust, when she, the mother, did not know how? *Example. I must give her an example.* Sue Ann experimented with a smile; her lips were stiff. *Jerry, help me!*

Sue Ann reached out with a tentative hand to his arm, faltered, clutched his white sleeve. He looked down at her and saw that she was frightened, and simply circled an arm around her back. It was not part of the ceremony, not done. Yet he did it. An arm around her to steady her. *Half a ring,* she thought. *And I am the other half.* Her legs stopped trembling as warmth coursed through her.

If he never backed her again, she thought, she would always be grateful that he'd supported her now. She smiled gratefully into his eyes. He grinned. It was inappropriate for a groom to grin as the minister intoned a prayer, yet Jerry's face cracked like her heart into a thousand happy lines.

She chuckled softly.

Jerry squeezed her hand.

Reverend Walker's voice quavered, "Do you, Jerald Teal, take this woman..."

For the briefest moment, Sue Ann looked at Serena. Their gazes held. Then, giving her a confident smile, Sue Ann turned to watch Jerry answer.

"Yes," he said, gazing happily at her, "I take her for my wife, my cherished wife."

Sue Ann's heart constricted with the sincerity she saw in his eyes. He'd ad-libbed the marriage vows, and it pleased her. It made her ecstatic. With a certainty that shook her, she knew she wanted his gray-green eyes always gazing at her as if he'd just found a precious stone. She wanted his lips to say again, "cherished wife." She wanted him with her, beside her, loving her for days without end. And then she promised, "I do," in a clear voice that surprised her with its intensity.

Reverend Walker said a prayer, holding a ring before them. It glittered with diamonds. Jerry took it, the ring he'd bought in Los Angeles after checking with Sue Ann, and, slipping the band of gold and diamonds over her finger, he said, "With this ring I thee wed."

Taking the college ring, she kissed it, smiled at Serena, and fitted it over Jerry's smallest finger. It went as far as the second knuckle because that was as far as it would go, and he grinned and it was all she could do not to give way to hysterical giggles. With as much decorum as she could muster, she repeated the pledge.

The minister pronounced them "man and woman, joined before God and all peoples as husband and wife." He beckoned them to kiss. Jerry's lips barely brushed Sue Ann's mouth, but his hands on her arms felt strong and sure. The reverend turned them, presented them, and the music swelled as Sue Ann and Jerry walked arm in arm down the aisle.

The wedding party followed, pouring through the heavy doors and down the rutted path strewn with straw. They caught up with Jerry and Sue Ann at the stone gateposts, where snow-laden boughs formed an arbor. There were congratulations, hugs, kisses. Sue Ann felt giddy and confused, and Jerry's arm slipped around her back, bracing her, not letting her go. The congregation came bubbling up to them, cheering, throwing rice that fell with the snowflakes to blend into the white carpet beneath their restless feet.

Tana squealed in delight. Eric scooped her up, nudged Laura ahead of him and motioned to Jerry, "C'mon. Make a run for it."

Laughing, they dashed across the spit of land to the shore, to the cars, Jerry and Sue Ann climbing into the back of a gray limousine she'd rented, and her brother, Laura and Tana piling into the front. Clint, Viv and Serena looked after the relatives, getting them from the church to the cars. Wearing his charcoal usher's coat and a pink shirt, Mel directed traffic, yelling instructions to someone stuck in the mud near the exit road.

Inside the limo, Eric gunned the motor. He flipped the door locks, then laughed like a banshee when the crowd pressed against the windows, pounding on the glass. "Last one to Douglas is a rotten egg!" he shouted, and swung the big car uphill, leading the wedding party on the fastest getaway in the history of Juneau.

Sue Ann chuckled.

"What are you laughing about?" said Jerry, scooting over to hug her.

"Eric." She nodded toward the smoked glass that separated them from the family. "Look at him. Taking charge, bossing everybody, acting like an overgrown Sir Lancelot. You'd think he was happy or something."

"And how about you?" He tightened his arms and bent until his breath pulsed against her lips. "How happy are you, Mrs. Teal?"

"Very happy," she said, feathering his lips with hers. "Except for your missing ring, the wedding went off without a hitch."

"Time out," he whispered, making her shiver with kisses on her neck.

"Time out for what?" she said, her voice falling away.

"Clint and the others are in charge now. You're off duty."

"You mean I've been fired, darling?"

"Promoted."

"To what?"

"Bride. Brides always take the day off after they get married. And the night—" he loosened the top button of her bodice "—and the next day—" he brushed her skin with a series of lowering kisses "—and the night after that . . ."

Giving way because her body remembered and wanted him, Sue Ann sank into the leather seat and wrapped her arms around her husband. They kissed, the first passion of marriage flaring between them. Speeding through the airport district, heading for the bridge to Douglas with their arms locked around each other, she thought fleetingly, *The ring, we are the ring . . .*

Chapter Eleven

"I'm so glad you didn't trash up your exit with those ridiculous tin cans dragging from the bumper, Sue Ann," Ester said, her chin tucked against her chest as if that would prevent the remaining hundred or so guests at the reception from knowing she was half in her cups. Ester waved toward the crowded floor, where couples and children gyrated to the rhythm of drums and guitars. "Kept the important things, though. You and Jerry leading the first waltz—'Lara's Theme,' wasn't it?—surprised this new-generation band had it in them. And that lovely cake, and the toasts from the best man and your brother and that Mel person. And all the political types who stopped by." Ester shook her head. "It's wonderful to see you among so many friends, looking so...settled. I suppose I'm being silly, rambling on about things you already know."

"Of course not, Aunt. I wanted a big reception. I wanted Juneau to know what a fine family I have," she said. "And that a couple of substance has just joined the ranks of the first families of Southeast."

"Well, you've achieved your goal, I'd say." Ester brandished a bony wrist in Sue Ann's direction, a diamond bracelet clacking against her watch. The hand landed on Sue Ann's shoulder and slipped off. "Entitled, at my age," she said.

Sue Ann retrieved her aunt's hand, shook her head "no" at Aunt Harriet, who was about to come to her rescue, and kissed Ester's cheek. "Entitled to what, at your age?" she asked.

"Entitled to get maudlin at your wedding, girl. Your Uncle Anthony sends his love, by the way. He's in Europe with that paper cartel, so I had to come by myself. Get all s-s-s—'' she sipped her champagne ''—sentimental by myself.''

"But you're not by yourself, Ester.''

"Am.''

"You're with Harriet and Brad, Serena, me, Eric and Laura. All your family.''

"Left out your new husband.'' Ester eyed her.

Sue Ann glanced through the crowd to the far side of the dining room. Jerry stood with Mel, no doubt talking shop. His white jacket faded into the glare of windows backed by falling snow. But he still stood out from the others. For one thing, he was the tallest man in the room. For another, his dark, silver-tipped hair made him look distinguished and ageless. Affection for him softened Sue Ann's voice as she murmured, "How odd that I would forget to mention Jerry. We'll be very happy, you know.''

"Good.'' She patted Sue Ann's hand. "You've always been one of my favorites, and when Bill died, why, you were so devastated I wondered whether . . .''

Sue Ann tensed, barely concentrating as her aunt scratched around in a brown leather purse trimmed in fur.

The memories of Bill and his tragic fate riddled Sue Ann's composure. Then something blurred by. Sue Ann looked up, forced a smile in response to Serena's wave as she swept past, heading toward the stairs. *No ghosts from the past will ruin this day,* Sue Ann affirmed. *Only the future matters—with Jerry.*

She looked for him, needing the contact. He was sampling a delicacy from the buffet and chatting with Laura and Tana. Sue Ann watched Tana prance for him, watched the child's face light with pleasure at some compliment Jerry paid her. It warmed Sue Ann, that vignette with her husband and niece. Her facial features relaxed.

Jerry glanced toward her. He winked conspiratorially, tapped his watch to remind Sue Ann it was nearly time to go. Her heart beat faster and she waved, nodded.

As he went back to talking with Laura and Tana, Sue Ann remembered his arm supporting her back, at the church. She thought of the snuggling they'd done in the limousine, risky because the family was in the front seat, and therefore more exciting, but safe because the glass was smoked, obscuring details, giving them privacy. And the waltz, she recalled, purposely rebuilding her confidence. They'd danced as if they'd been dancing together for years.

She turned to Ester, interrupting her investigation into the brown purse to say distinctly, "Bill's memory is sacred because of Serena, Ester. But Jerry and I are the future."

"Yes, yes, dear. Delightful boy, your Jerry. If I could only find the damned envelope."

"Aunt." Sue Ann laughed, relaxing. "You never use profanity."

"Of course I don't. Ah!" She held up a white envelope. "Your wedding gift, Sue Ann."

The legacy. Sue Ann stared at it, her pulse jumping. At last she could tell Jerry. She could tell Eric. Already the weight of secrecy was lifting from her, letting her breathe as if for the first moment in months.

Ester thrust the envelope into her hand. "If I'd put it in the back of the car with all the other presents, it might have gotten lost," she whispered with exaggerated confidentiality. "In my condition—not that it's noticeable—I might have stuck it under the window washers." She giggled. "Well, open it, Sue Ann. You already know what it is."

"Yes." She felt breathless, elated.

"Everyone always knows what I give."

"Little white envelopes," said Sue Ann, slipping a finger under the flap to break the seal. "Your generosity is legendary. And don't think for a minute we don't know what's behind it."

"What?"

"Love."

"Nonsense," she snorted. "I just can never think of what people want. Other than money, of course. Everyone wants more of that. Why not give what's easiest to give?"

"Oh, Aunt, you always underrate yourself."

Looking benign, Ester picked up her glass and sipped.

Sue Ann pulled out a card and began to read, "To the newlyweds," but something fluttered to the floor. She bent, picked up a personal check and saw the amount—$200,000. Her breathing held. The legacy was only supposed to be $50,000.

And then she realized she'd misread the check, and her breath came fast as her eyes riveted on the correct amount: $2000.

Stunned and confused, she could only stare at it.

"Heavens," said her aunt, "it's only a couple of thousand, not the Franklin Mint. Are you sure you and Jerry will be all right financially, dear? If not, I'll write another—"

"No," said Sue Ann, finding her voice. She shook her head. "Jerry's well off. I'm just so... surprised."

"Don't know why you should be. I realize you've had a good career, but there are always little expenses that crop up at a wedding. And besides, I simply didn't know what else the two of you would like. If you don't need it, why, put it away for Serena's career—new portfolio, suits for interviews, that kind of thing." Ester gripped her arm as if she suddenly realized a scary possibility. "Sue Ann. You don't think your man will be offended, my giving money?"

"Not in the least, Aunt," she said, her gaze playing over the guests, a frown rippling her forehead. *Who, then, she wondered. Who had given her the legacy? And why?* She spotted Eric, her closest family member, talking with Mel and Sam Gord. Eric as benefactor was out of the question. From the very beginning, his company had been on thin ice. The mine contract would get them out of debt and leave a little extra for a vacation or new equipment for the company, but no more. Harriet and Brad? She watched her gray-haired aunt dab at her husband's suit coat, where he'd spilled his drink. They'd been married thirty-five years and were well-off. In five years, Brad would retire from the presidency of a leading Seattle bank. But Sue Ann had never been particularly close with them. They sent Christmas cards, she called them once a year at Easter.

Then who could it have been? She'd been wracking her brain since the letter arrived last January, and now there seemed to be only one other possibility. Mark. But she didn't even want to think of that, couldn't bear to ruin today. This day was sacred to her and Jerry. Yet Mark might stand between them. Obscure... but there.

Suddenly she had to see Mel, and she stood. It took all her will to bend to Ester, hug her warmly and reassure her the $2000 would come in handy for a certain vacation she and Jerry were planning—someplace islandy, romantic, expensive. Then she motioned to Harriet to come visit Ester, and Sue Ann went to find Mel, who'd said, years ago, that Mark had asked about her.

Hurrying around the tables, she spotted Mel, the sleeves of his gray jacket pushed up, his tie loosened. He stood beside Eric, both of them looking toward the stairs.

Everyone was looking, she realized. Halfway down the staircase, Serena stood staring up at a stranger of about thirty-five. He wore a charcoal London Fog, the shoulders speckled with snow. He had bearing, Sue Ann noted, but a frayed bearing, as if he were strung out, going on nerves.

Sue Ann made it to the foot of the stairs before she felt Jerry's arm come around her. It was a brief contact, meant to let her know he was with her. They hurried up to Serena, who was greeting the stranger.

Jerry spoke from two steps away: "Stone?" and climbed up next to the man. They were the same height. "Mickey Stone?" said Jerry. "Sue Ann said you'd be coming."

The man nodded curtly, still looking harried.

Sounding as smooth as a seasoned diplomat, Jerry said, "I'm Jerry Teal." He indicated Sue Ann, who put an arm around Serena. "My wife, Sue Ann."

He bent his head in acknowledgment. "I apologize for being delayed, Mrs. Teal."

"None of us counted on the snowstorm, Mr. Stone. I'm relieved you arrived safely." After introducing Serena, Sue Ann added, "Come down and meet my family and friends, have a drink, some smoked salmon. Do you like seafood? Alaska has the best."

"Thank you, Mrs. Teal, but I couldn't." He glanced upstairs. "Is there somewhere private . . ."

Jerry touched her sleeve. "The lobby."

Serena went back down to the guests as Sue Ann, Jerry and Mickey Stone climbed to the lobby. They followed Stone to a window near the entrance doors where he drew a black velvet box from his coat pocket.

"I'm truly sorry I couldn't get in yesterday. I've . . . been on a case for several months and just before I was due to take off, I got a break and had to check it out."

"Case?" said Sue Ann, trying to follow the whereabouts of the velvet box—it was tucked into Stone's hand, and he had let his arm slacken to his side. "What case is that, Mr. Stone?"

"Mickey, please." He stared out into the snow for a moment. "Garden Emerald," he said, his eyes narrowing, his voice lowering an octave, a kind of bitterness cutting through his exhaustion. Sue Ann recognized emotional pain when she heard it. It was as if mentioning the emerald scraped an old wound.

Stone turned. His eyes were bloodshot, but his gaze was steady, frank. "Unfortunately, the emerald got in the way of my bringing your ring on time."

Abruptly he held out the box to Sue Ann.

She took it. It was awkward to have to look at the ring now, in front of a stranger. She'd wanted Jerry to have it at the wedding ceremony, with pomp and circumstance making the gift special.

Stone rummaged in a hidden pocket of his coat. He brought out a paper, a pen. He handed them to Sue Ann. "If you'll just look over the ring," he said. "Make sure it's what you ordered, sign for it, then I'll be on my way."

Sue Ann simply glanced at the ring, signed the receipt and thanked him. With a grim smile, Mickey Stone pushed through the door and disappeared in a haze of white.

Jerry winked at Sue Ann. "How come I feel like Cinderella all of a sudden, Mrs. Teal?"

"Because I've got the glass slipper?"

He nudged her chin. "Let's see if it fits."

Tucking the paperwork into his jacket pocket, Sue Ann opened the box. The ring was exactly what she'd ordered, the one-karat diamond set flush in geometric shapes of platinum, silver and white gold, not a sharp edge anywhere, the stone and the metals gleaming like the Aurora Borealis.

"Good Lord in heaven," said Jerry.

She glanced up. He looked shocked. His jaw was slack. "Give me your hand, Jerry," she said, buoyed because she'd impressed him, just as she'd planned.

He held out his left hand. She plucked off the college ring and slipped it into his pocket. Then she slid the wedding ring onto his finger, easing it over his second knuckle. The completion she'd waited for surged over her, the electricity arched between them, and she fought past a lump in her throat to say, "With this ring I thee wed."

A long moment passed during which they could not look away from one another.

"Sue Ann," Jerry said. "I want you to know I love you."

"Why?" she breathed, caught in a moment so dear to her she knew she would never forget it.

"For how hard you try to please," he said. "Anything is possible with a spirit like yours. You have my love. I can wait for yours."

She closed her eyes. Inside, she shook a little. A year's worth of anguish and doubt collided with hope and happiness. Blindly, she reached out her hand. He caught it, turned up her palm and kissed it. She opened her eyes. She and Jerry drifted together, brushed lips, lingering over the kiss and wanting more, but aware of the guests downstairs.

Sue Ann smiled lazily. "I guess this means you don't like it," she whispered.

"You have no idea.... For the first time in years, I feel anchored but not stuck. I belong here with you. Let's go home, Sue Ann."

Arms around each other, they moved to the stairs and urged the guests to gather below them, single women and girls clustered in the foreground. Serena brought up the bride's bouquet. Sue Ann faced away, preparing to toss the flowers. Mel sneaked into the knot of women, causing a stir, then embarrassed himself by catching the bouquet, and his antics provided the gaiety upon which Jerry and Sue Ann made their escape.

Half an hour passed before Sue Ann remembered why she'd been looking for Mel. By then they were caught behind a snowplow that crept along, clearing the highway, lights blinking. She changed down to low gear, resigned to a slow ride to the cabin. Jerry made a comment about the Department of Transportation conspiring to test his patience.

Sue Ann was just turning to smile at him when she remembered. The inheritance. A last detail left dangling in an otherwise idyllic moment of her life.

Jerry's hand slid along her thigh. "You keep driving," he said, grinning. "I'll start the honeymoon."

"Honeymoons are a two-party system."

"Uh-huh." He slid his hand beneath her skirt, and sensation spiraled into her midsection, temporarily rendering the question of the money irrelevant.

Chapter Twelve

As they entered the county road leading to the cabin turnoff, Jerry sat up and watched Sue Ann bully the Subaru around the curves, admiring her skill.

"Way to go, sourdough," he said, patting her thigh.

She smiled, shifted into second for a tight downhill turn, then crept over a wooden bridge. Black ponds flanked the bridge, the snow denting the water with thousands of tiny ringlets. It looked eerie, as if the ponds dirtied the purity of the landscape.

"Good trout fishing here," said Sue Ann, evidently misreading his thoughts. "I recall you like to fish."

"I forgot to ask . . . do you?"

"If they're biting. These guys in here like worms or cheese. That usually keeps us both busy. Me and the trout, I mean."

Shaking his head, he reached for her thigh again—he couldn't seem to keep his hands off her. "You're a constant surprise," he said.

She drove on, a smile on her lips.

Deeper into the wilderness, the evergreens were iced like Christmas candles. A snowplow had been down in here this morning, Sue Ann told him, clearing the route to Amalga Harbor. Snowbanks rimmed the road, forming a frosty moat between the lanes of undergrowth.

Slowing to a stop and pointing to the edge of a meadow, Sue Ann said, "Jerry, look."

He followed her arm. "I'll be," he mused, craning forward. "A great big daddy Bambi."

About fifty yards away, a white-tailed buck nibbled at branches above his head, his brown withers and back collecting powder. His antlers caught in the leaves. He shook, showering himself with snow. Backing away, darting a look at the car, the deer bolted into the woods.

Pleased about the unexpected deer, Jerry turned to Sue Ann, and the pleasure deepened when he eyed her profile, the way the light hit her chest and shadowed the underside of her breasts. God, she was beautiful. He scooted over and ran his hands over her waist, midriff, breasts. Sensation jolted through him. Sue Ann's breath caught, held.

He chuckled and nipped her neck.

She gripped the steering wheel harder. "Dear Lord, we can make it home. I know we can."

Jerry laughed out loud. "All right, bride. Home. And then we'll see what other surprises we can discover."

"Agreed," she said under her breath.

Slinging the shift lever into first, she gunned the engine and tore down the road.

Jerry sat back, smiling. It was going to be fine, snuggling up to a fireplace with Sue Ann. He corrected himself: snuggling up to the stove. *Home.* He savored the word, the images it brought. The knowledge that she was strong and independent was such a plus. There probably wouldn't be much of that emotional heartache that had turned his insides to ice when he'd been married the first time.

It was too bad his L.A. cronies couldn't have seen him up there with his bride, he thought, grinning, feeling proud of himself. They'd have razzed him about it for hours. But Clint had been there. He'd share the news. Still, it would have been nice to have a few of his other buddies around.

He should have spoken to Sue Ann about it days, weeks ago. But she'd had such momentum going with her plans. And, somehow, when he was with her he wasn't thinking about his old life-style; he was locked in on those California-blue eyes.

Anyway, he told himself, he was already getting a whole bunch of new buddies to pal around with, so he felt at home, hardly missed his friends. He'd keep in touch by phone, and dig into life in Alaska.

Jerry glanced at Sue Ann. Maybe he could make it this time. Maybe home with Sue Ann was going to last.

Turning right, Sue Ann jammed the shift lever into second and barreled down a short lane and straight into the space widened for parking cars. She turned off the key, stuck it in her suit pocket, and took her foot off the clutch. The car coasted, shuddered to a stop.

For a moment she looked straight ahead into the curtain of snowflakes. Then she turned. Staring at one another for a moment, they burst into laughter.

"This feels strange," she said when it had gotten quiet again. She reached behind her to open the door, letting in a woodsy draft. "Coming home with you."

"Get used to it. We'll be doing a lot of it."

"I'm glad, Jerry. Glad it's all over and we can just be...us." He cuddled her cool cheek with his palm. "Tired?"

"Emotionally, a little. All the pressure. Physically I feel like a champ. How about you?"

"Fine...." Something odd about the scent of the wind urged him to look outside. "You smell something funny? Like burnt hoses or electrics?"

"No." She squinted at the sky. "What's that up there?"

He looked above the treeline. A couple of black slivers blinked in the blizzard and faded.

Suddenly Sue Ann bolted from the car.

After a stunned moment, Jerry followed, cursing her speed, her familiarity with the path down which she'd disappeared.

He came charging into the edge of the clearing. He was only a yard behind her when Sue Ann cried out, put her hands over her mouth, and sank into his arms as if someone had punched her.

"What the devil, Sue Ann—?"

She made odd, gasping sounds, her eyes trained in horror at the cabin, forty or fifty feet down the hill.

"Holy Mother of God!" Jerry said.

The roof of the cabin looked as if it had been struck by a grenade. Wisps of smoke curled from a hole big enough to drive a car through. The surrounding shingles looked sweat-stained, and sooty runoff streaked the patches of snow cling-ing to the eaves. Timber creaked and hissed.

"Easy, Sue Ann," Jerry crooned, his heart thundering. He tried to readjust her weight so he could cradle her.

But she snapped to her feet and darted down the board-walk. Jerry ran, slipped, recovered himself. "Sue Ann, don't go—"

Pounding up the three stairs, she shoved open the door. Smoke billowed out. She clawed her way through it.

"Could explode," Jerry shouted, catching up, grabbing her shoulders and pulling her around. The stench of burning cloth, wood and wire assailed them. Smoke stung his eyes. He drew it into his lungs, coughed. She began to slip away, and he hooked her arm to drag her back.

"Sue Ann, it's dangerous!"

"Let go! Got to save my cabin!" She struggled, pummeled him.

Sue Ann had the strength of a pro wrestler, her agony pumping adrenaline through her bloodstream and firing her muscles with lightning. She twisted again and managed to yank away.

A high-pitched cry, and she crashed into the wall on his right. The paneling collapsed, splintering with a dry hiss, sifting the air with ash. She fell into the storage room and scrambled away.

He lunged after her, his hand grazing the wall, registering warmth.

Steam hissed and rose into smoke, blackened beams and shards angled everywhere, the stovepipe swung from a rafter like an elbow broken and bent the wrong way. In a corner hulked Serena's old twin bed, stacked with his shipping trunks, untouched. Snow filtered down through the hole in the roof onto piles of half-burned split logs, and light layered through a ragged opening in the wall to his left—the wall that should have backed the potbellied stove. He knew instantly a spark had leaped from the stove to the wood she kept stacked along the living-room wall. In that brief instant of scrutiny, he saw that the stove had toppled over onto the brick hearth, but the bricks had protected most of the oak flooring. And the snow had retarded the flames. She was lucky. He heard a whimper and, startled, peered through the gloom.

Panting like a winded lioness, her hair a gold blur in a charcoal cave, Sue Ann scrambled over debris. "Mark," she said in a stage whisper, crawling past beams glistening with moisture. "Oooh, Mark, the pain is bad, very bad. Hide at the cabin."

Who the hell is Mark, Jerry thought. But maybe it was just a name from her childhood—he felt his brain hazing, too, from lack of oxygen. He struggled to focus on Sue Ann. She seemed more affected by the smoke than he, more disoriented. He reached for her, but she stepped away. He muttered, tried again, coughing, feeling light-headed.

"Bill?" she asked.

The smoke was really getting to her, he thought, feeling panicked. One of them had to stay alert. Tearing off his jacket, ripping out the lining, he soaked the silk in melted snow and tied it around his nose and mouth. He dragged in a few breaths of air. It tasted and smelled of charcoal, but the smoke was filtered out. Now he could get Sue Ann. He stood still and held out his hand to her, spoke to her. She rolled across a heap of wood coals, streaking her suit with black, and broke into the living room. She darted here and there between grotesque shapes that had once been lamps, tables. She hugged a huge rocker-lounge and wailed. Gagging, crying, stamping at cinders, the smoke swirling around her, Sue Ann caught up a charred red blanket he remembered from a lifetime ago, and looked around, her eyes crazy.

It was heartrending. Jerry's heart plunged. He leaped for her. She ducked away, dodging past a smoldering corner of the couch. Her shoes crunched on glass. The sound ripped through him, shattering his reason. Despite his makeshift mask, coughs rocked his body. Everything loomed black or gray, smoldering. Like death. *Too much emotion. I can't cope.*

Under his feet, the rug curled—charred, soaked with melted snow—the snow was a blessing; it had saved her cabin. Most of it. *Help her,* said a voice from years ago. *She needs you.* "Sue Ann," he called, his voice sounding distant.

She hesitated for an instant—the fleeing animal called by its mate. Then she moaned and grabbed at pillows, magazines. Despair pierced his heart. Her desperation...he wanted to run from it, get away from such great pain. *No. Face it. I'm dy-*

ing, Jerry. Be brave. Who had said that to him? Someone dying . . .

He shook his head. "Sue Ann?"

In answer, he heard a whimper.

She needs you. His wife needed him, but then she needed him all the time, always pulling at him, crying; he couldn't stand the suffocation, not with his mother dying of cancer— No, he corrected, *Sue Ann* needed him this time. Strong, capable Sue Ann. She'd never pulled at him, never demanded he breathe the same air she breathed. The smoke had dulled his brain. And then he remembered: he'd divorced his first wife, his mother had died, and Sue Ann was his new bride, his hope. He loved her. With her, he would be strong, as she was; without Sue Ann he would be empty.

These conclusions startled him. He stumbled toward her, his breath wheezing.

She was a wild thing, evading the lunges he made to catch her, leaping up on the couch, heaving herself over it and falling against the charred table. As it gave way beneath her, she caught up bits of china shattered by the fire at its zenith.

"No-ooo!" she wailed, diving for a small object that had fallen in the cinders. She clutched it to her, rocking and crying. "Jerry?" she said in a small voice. "Where are you, Jerry?"

Again that spike pierced his heart. "Here, sweetheart," he heard himself say. "I'm here. Always . . . be here for you."

She did not even look up when he gathered her in his arms and carried her out of the cabin.

THE JACKALS OF THE CITY circled in to sniff at her ankles. The beasts of the woods breathed stench into her face and tore at her with acid-sharp claws. The teeth of the wilderness ground into her, and she had nothing left to fight it. She writhed in fear.

From black to white. From dark cave to emergency room. Jerry had taken her to doctors, she remembered through a gauzy veil of sedative. When? Hours ago? Days?

Then, back to his hotel room. He'd washed her face, hands, legs . . . so good, soft, warm . . . hands like angels' wings. He'd made the jackals fade back into the trees. She wore his white silk shirt with the pleats, so the beasts couldn't recognize her.

Hot now, too hot. Covers heavy. How hard it was to lift them, toss them somewhere. Ah... "Yes, better," she whispered.

The curtain of drugs lifted, and she remembered. But only some of it.

It had taken a lifetime to stop shaking, moaning, clutching—clutching at anything, the door handle in the car, Jerry's sleeve, the doctor's smock, the bud vase.

She hugged the slender porcelain object to her stomach, reassured by its shape, and burrowed deeper into the covers, drifting.

Jerry's voice hummed in the background. "Calmed down quite a bit... sleeping now," he said to someone. "Fire department... hose from the bay to the cabin, pumping water..."

Don't listen, she thought. There was something frightening she must not think about, and to listen would be to know. She looked at the flowers flowing over the bedspread, at the streaks of shadow on the draperies. Everything familiar, clean—not like her, sooty and broken inside. No, not sooty. Clean, now, but still broken.

There was a detail she hadn't cleared up; maybe that was why she suffered so. She'd always known if she didn't take care of things, it would get bad, very bad. She must—

Struggling through mountains of gauze, she turned and slid over. She felt something warm and curved in her hand—the bud vase; she'd have to leave it. She had to take care of that business of the money. She pushed the vase beneath the pillow, where it would be safe.

Easing up, she sat on the edge of the big bed. The floor looked very far away, and a hurricane spun in her head.

Get up, take care of it, she thought. From far away, she heard a whisper. Then a roar: "Sue Ann!"

Frightened, she cowered.

But his hands feathered her arms, and his voice softened. "Sue Ann, honey, where are you going?"

"Detail," she said, mouthing the word around cotton. "Take care of the detail."

"What detail, Sue Ann?"

"The—the—m-money."

Oh, you've told him and he won't love you now. He'll think you tricked him. He'll go away. "Don't go!" She clutched him tightly. "Bill, Mark—now you!"

Blackness began to descend again, but she fought it and began to moan, "Jerry, the cabin, save the cabin."

But he couldn't save it. It had been destroyed by fire. *Ah, God, not safe anymore.* Tears took over again, wracking her body. Jerry held her, crooning, keeping the jackals at bay.

"Lie down, Sue Ann." She obeyed the gentle voice. "That's good. Sleep for a while."

Curling her fingers in his shirt, she pleaded, "Jerry, the cabin's gone."

"I know, darling."

"What will we do?"

"We'll build it again."

So simple. Build it again. She felt a small stab of hope. "Yes," she said, releasing him and lying back. "We'll be safe then."

A ring is just a ring, Mama. It's people that count. Not things.

SUE ANN WOKE to darkness and a fluttering sound. A faint pain flashed through her temples. Instantly she realized she'd been in shock. The cabin had burned, and she'd gone temporarily out of her mind, the hysteria muddled later by drugs.

The ache of losing the cabin still wound through her, making her feel sad, but the fact that she and Jerry were facing the setback together took the edge off the loss. They would rebuild, he'd said last night. Tomorrow they could plan the reconstruction. It would all be okay.

The fluttering sound penetrated her thoughts. Jerry's breathing—light snoring, actually, she thought, her features breaking into a smile. Probably exhausted by the events of the day, he was sleeping as if he were the one who'd taken the sedative. How homey it felt, hearing him in the darkness, feeling his warmth behind her.

And to think of his strength of character! She now had an inkling of what he'd been like with his mother during her illness—patient, tender, level-headed. Sue Ann guessed she had her proof now that Jerry would stand by her. Instead of handing her off to somebody else during some of the worst moments she'd been through in the past twenty years, he'd taken care of her himself. On their wedding day! If this didn't test his love, his reliability, nothing would.

Feeling grateful and affectionate, she twisted as carefully as she could, lay on her back, and put a hand on the covers draping his hip. The snoring stopped, and Jerry cuddled closer and wrapped his arm around her.

Sue Ann lay awake for a while, wondering if the new, sweet pain in her heart was love.

IN THE MORNING she rose before Jerry was awake and went into the bathroom to survey the damage to her face. Puffy eyes. A gray smudge under her nose. Hair that looked like dirty straw. This wouldn't do, she thought. Not on their first morning as husband and wife.

A heaviness hung just the other side of her natural morning energy, trying to bring her down, but she refused to carry the burden of regret. She and Jerry would rebuild. A wonderful project for newlyweds. Setting her shoulders in determination, she looked around.

The tan carpet stopped at the bathroom, where beige-and-gold floor tiles spread from the sink cabinet to the tub and the frosted-glass door. The white bathtub reminded her briefly of her kitchen counters—gleaming ceramic tiles and grout she scrubbed with bleach and an old toothbrush to keep it pristine. She disliked the muted colors hotels used so they wouldn't offend any of the great mix of guests in such places. She told herself not to fret; these were temporary quarters. Soon she would be moving back to her familiar country home. She could hardly wait to begin the journey.

Showering away the residue of the fire, toweling off her hair and body, Sue Ann began a mental list of the tasks involved in rebuilding the cabin. It must be put back stock, as they said in the car industry. The same kind of stove, the same draperies and braided rug.

It would be awfully expensive, she supposed. But finances were already halfway arranged, as if, knowing the tragic loss she would face, Providence had laid before her the wherewithal to begin again.

First of all, she had Ester's gift of $2000. Plus the insurance payoff, of course. And then, the legacy would be arriving.

She combed her hair, musing about the inheritance. Even the origin of the money seemed less important now, after the trauma of the fire. With Jerry beside her, an old ghost didn't seem so scary. So what if Mark had set up the legacy? If she found out it was him, she would refuse the money. If she never found out who it was from—well, she refused to lose sleep over it. Why look a gift horse in the mouth? And if the inheritance had to be returned to sender, she was sure Jerry wouldn't mind putting a few thousand toward the renovation. She already had proof of his generosity and his devotion to her. And, after all, it would be his home, too.

Things were beginning to look bright. She was always at her best in the morning. Slipping into the silk shirt, she grinned, thinking she ought to go wake him up, put her energy to good use. She'd have to remember to warn Jerry about her energy in the morning.

"Sexy," he said from the doorway.

She turned, blushing. "Hi..."

He blinked sleepily, then smiled and opened his arms to her. "Morning hug," he said.

She went to him and put her arms around his waist, her cheek against his shoulder. He wore underwear and a gray shirt of brushed cotton, which was more than she had on. His legs felt fuzzy and warm.

"Your grandmother's china, Jerry. I think most of it's ruined."

"Never mind," he said, rocking her a little. "We'll go to London and buy some of our own. My grandmother would understand." He pulled back. "How are you feeling, babe?"

"Grateful." She squeezed him. "So very glad you're my husband."

He kissed the top of her head. "We'll rebuild, Sue Ann."

"I know. I've been trying to decide where to start, what to do first."

She rattled on about filing an insurance claim, asking Eric's advice about a construction crew, ordering a new stove. Even while Jerry took his turn in the bathroom, Sue Ann called out plans to him: "We'll have to order a new wood stove and pipe." And, while dialing for room service: "Any idea where I can find a braided rug as big as the ruined one? It was there when I bought the place. Do you want orange juice and coffee, darling?"

"Yes," he said. "Are you always like this?"

"Always—wait a minute—yes, room service?" When she'd placed the order, she set down the receiver, picked up her pen, and called out to Jerry, "I meant to warn you about my energy in the mornings."

"I take a while to get rolling."

"Jerry Teal," she laughed. "I recall getting a phone call from you one day at 6:00 a.m."

"That was different. I was courting you."

She pursed her lips. "Are you shaving yet?"

"Uh-huh."

"Want me to do it for you?"

A pause. He chuckled. "Not under the circumstances." She laughed.

"Say, Sourdough—" A bottle, probably his after-shave, clinked on the counter. She heard slapping sounds. "I think we ought to consider expanding a bit on the west side. The kitchen and dining areas could use some breathing room."

His comment jarred her, shadowed her glib mood. "But I love the kitchen. I can reach everything in four steps. By the way, what kind of shingling is on the roof? Cedar?"

He muttered a reply. She would ask him again later, she thought, jotting down several ideas. A few minutes later, the door rattled. Sue Ann interrupted her listing of supplies on hotel stationery long enough to see the refreshments laid out on the table and to sign the room-service check. Then she went back to writing.

Jerry stepped out of the dressing area. "What're you doing?" he asked.

"Making a list of people we have to call. Things we have to buy."

He laughed, sounding incredulous. "For the cabin?"

"Yes. We can get started first thing tomorrow morning. In fact, I was thinking of calling Eric to ask him to line up a contractor today."

"I don't believe it."

His flat tone of voice made her look up. Bare-chested and wearing no shoes, he stood just inside the room, an arm propped on the dresser. Still damp, his hair shone. A spark of something—frustration, anger?—made his eyes look as if they were smoldering. He reminded her of one of those James Dean or Jack Nicholson types who were always driving women wild with moody expressions and dramatic poses. He wore thigh-hugging jeans of a faded blue. She noticed the top button of his jeans was undone, black hair curling from the opening.

Suddenly her energy rechanneled itself. Lowering her voice, she said, "Oh, my, Jerry."

He had the panache to flex his pectorals and smile. "That's more like it," he said.

"Sexy. Very sexy."

"Come here and say that."

A flame ignited in her. Holding his gaze, she put down the pen and walked slowly across the room. She ran her fingertips through the salt-and-pepper hair on his chest, down to the swirl at his jeans opening, all the while staring at him, watching the expressions change and flow over his face. She nudged his zipper down. Just a little. His jaw slackened, his eyes darkened. Imperceptibly, his breathing shallowed out. Her heart thudding, she trailed her fingers up his abdomen to a dark-pink nipple. A moan floated from him, and he closed his eyes.

"Yes," she whispered. "It's my turn. My turn to make you feel good, sweetheart."

"Sue Ann." He moved to embrace her.

"No, baby. My turn." Sue Ann bent to his arm, floated her lips along his skin. She slid one of his hands back to the dresser, the other to the door molding. As Jerry closed his eyes, leaning back against the wall, Sue Ann saw his chest expand and contract, and she shuddered, her body tingling with longing.

Chapter Thirteen

As it turned out, most of Sue Ann's plans were tabled till Monday, and she had no complaints.

On Sunday morning, Jerry gave her another gift from his luggage, a kelly-green satin teddy with lace Vs at the hips and neckline. When she modeled it for him, they couldn't let it go at that.

Between lovemaking sessions, she and Jerry tracked the whereabouts of family and friends. They called Douglas so Sue Ann could reassure Serena she was all right, and learned that Eric and Mel had gone out to see the cabin. At 11:00 a.m. she had the report from Eric. Everything in the cabin was soaked and blackened, and badly chopped up as a result of the efforts of the fire department to ensure nothing else would burn, he said. He and Mel had lashed together some tarpaulins and covered the hole in the roof. She relayed the information to Jerry, who, while listening to her and watching a TV program on fishing, had been caressing her.

When Eric had reassured Sue Ann he'd think about the right crew for the reconstruction, she asked what the rest of the family was doing. He handed the phone to Serena.

Clint, Viv, and the relatives who'd stayed in town were coming over to visit and sample the leftovers from the buffet, said her daughter. Vivian had agreed to drop off some clothes Laura was getting together for Sue Ann. She and Jerry were invited over, but since Jerry was in a honeymoon mood, Sue Ann sent her love and declined.

When they'd hung up, Sue Ann curled around to lie beside Jerry. They chatted for a while, then Jerry got up to close the draperies. He turned off the television and switched on soft music. They lay together again, whispering, touching, beginning to move together as Jerry murmured against her ear about the way her body thrilled him.

And she began to tease him with her body, rolling her torso against his chest, playing her fingertips and nails in patterns on his back and buttocks. He braced his body against her onslaught, but she persisted, her lips lingering in spirals on his chest, trailing up his throat; hot eager legs wrapping him, begging him. Ah, the grace that came to her body when they loved, she thought, still kissing him as she reached beyond his shoulder to snap out the lamp.

The accordion folds of the draperies cast them in shadow and light. Faster came Jerry's breathing. He looked down at Sue Ann's face. Shadowed gray-green eyes drew her with a magnetism she felt in the depths of her. Brushing her hair from her eyes in a way that was tender yet urgent, he bowed against her. She relaxed her muscles to blend with him a moment, then held back. His desire was like a brook tumbling over her, catching her unaware, sweeping her with a freshness, an aliveness that made her cry out. When she cried, he surged against her. Then Jerry held himself still as she clung to him, the restraint shuddering through him—and thrust again.

This game they played—waiting an unbearably long time before joining—heightened the pleasure. The desire became a need, a driving force laced with anticipation, so that breathing attuned, flesh bloomed with heat and trembled; and they clung to each other like the branches hold the leaves in a wind. Trembling, waiting to fall.

I love you, she thought. But she did not say it. Ever the restraint, the waiting, even in this. *He can look into my eyes and see that I feel it, this aching for him, this deep, deep caring.* It was love. It was. She would tell him.

The thought went like a secret message to him. She knew he could sense her emotion by the tender way he held her.

And the waiting ended.

SOMEONE POUNDED on the door—fierce hard knocking—and Jerry bolted up to see the mountains of Douglas Island glittering in sunlight. Cold, brittle light bounced off the snow and made him squint.

Frowsy and golden, Sue Ann angled up from under the covers and looked at him. "Someone's at the door," she said.

He caressed her shoulder, hating to lose the privacy. "I'll get it," he said. "Probably your clothes."

She lay back down. Tucking the covers around her, he twisted out of bed and rummaged for his jeans, pulled them on.

A blinking light on the telephone caught his eye. They had messages—after watching the sun set last night, they'd shared a steak dinner and champagne, and he'd asked the desk to hold their calls.

The pounding commenced again. "All right," he said, heading for the door. He hated to be roused so suddenly in the morning. It never boded well for someone to fire his blood first thing, unless it was for something as soul-stirring as loving Sue Ann.

The thundering outside began once more, and Jerry flipped the latch and yanked open the door, muttering, "Why didn't you just leave—"

Eric fell toward him. Jerry shouldered aside, put out a hand to steady him. Wearing a wool coat of tan plaid, his hair sticking out in all directions, Eric turned like a cornered tiger and gripped both of Jerry's arms.

"I tried to call. There's trouble with the project."

Sue Ann called shrilly, "Eric—" and groped for something to wrap in. She hurried into the dressing room.

"Slow down, man," said Jerry, closing the door and pulling Eric into the room. "What happened?"

"They shut us down!"

"Who did?"

"The environmentalists." Eric strode to the window, to the TV, to the table. He picked up a knife, juggled it. Suddenly he sent it crashing against last night's dinner plates. "I'm finished!"

Sue Ann came out wearing Jerry's gray bathrobe—it was the wrong color for her, he noted, distracted, tense. Gray bleached her skin. She stopped a yard away, her eyes big, her hands wrapped tightly against her stomach. It flashed through Jerry's mind that she ought not to withstand a great deal more stress right now, not after all she'd been through. That left him to handle Eric.

Forcing his voice to go smooth, he gestured to his brother-in-law. "What can I do to help?"

The distraught man glanced at him, looked away. "I haven't got much right. Not after the way I treated you."

"Forget all that," he waved. "What's behind the shutdown?"

"A damn salmon stream. The environmentalists came into camp late Friday. I should have been there. I might have reasoned with them, but I—" He angled his eyes at Jerry and Sue Ann, a regretful look that said he should never have left his crew to come to the wedding. And then he shrugged bitterly. "When they saw we'd decided to run the access road across one portion of the stream bed, they told my crew supervisor the road might wipe out the salmon run. With those people, there's no compromise. They shut us down."

"Can't you cut the road in another spot?"

"Don't you think we tried? There's no other way into the mine. Steep gorges and solid rock—cost a fortune to run a road up the side of the mountains. My client can't afford that. The only reason I got this job is because I figured I could run the best crew around practically day and night, get the job done in two months and get out."

He stalked to the window again, looked out.

His movement drew Sue Ann like a magnet. She followed him. "Eric, does this mean you're—"

"Broke?" He laughed. "That's it. I fronted the money for fuel, supplies, equipment, a helicopter, quality people. A gamble, Sue Ann. I gambled that I could do it."

"But maybe your client will do something," she offered. "Extend the budget, the time-to-completion."

"I tried that angle. You know what he said?"

"What?"

"He wants to 'reevaluate' the cost-effectiveness of opening the mine next spring. That means he's strung out too far. It's only clear to me now, after talking to him, how much of a shoestring he was working on, how desperately he wanted a cheap way to get in there. And I gave it to him.'' His voice went husky. ''Only it didn't work and I'm ruined.''

Tears welled, glistened in her eyes. She looked sideways at Jerry.

He came to her and put an arm around her. To Eric he said, ''You're here, man. You must think I can do something.''

Eric turned slowly. His gaze grazed Sue Ann's face, a touch of apology in his eyes. Then he fastened Jerry with a desperate look. ''Mel's a good man,'' he said, gesturing. ''My best friend, but he only pushes a pencil. He doesn't...study things, think about them much. He's done my taxes for several years.''

''Did he louse them up?''

''No,'' Eric said sharply. ''Nothing like that. I just...can't go to him with this.''

''With what, exactly?''

''The whole mess. I-I've been trying to keep things together. You know, do some of the financial stuff myself, run the numbers, keep track of payables and receivables, that kind of stuff. To cut costs. I don't know much about bookwork, I'm not good at it, but I know it's all pretty hopeless. You're a big-city financial man. I thought maybe...''

''I'll come down. Take a look.''

Eric gave Jerry a grateful look, a glance Jerry recognized. He'd seen it on Sue Ann's face at church two days ago. An age ago. He was in a rush suddenly to have the emotions ebb out of the crisis. Numbers he could handle. The morass of people's emotions was another matter.

''Give me a minute to get dressed,'' he said to Eric. ''I don't know what I can do, but we'll give it a shot.''

Eric's shoulders braced. ''I'll be downstairs. Look—'' He hesitated, sent another look of apology to Sue Ann.

''Forget it,'' said Jerry, thinking Eric felt badly about disrupting their honeymoon. He walked him to the door, grinning to ease the awkwardness. ''I love an accounting challenge. Puts lead in my pencil.''

Eric's face cracked into an unwilling smile.

Jerry let him out, spotted a brown paper bag with a note on hotel stationery attached to it with tape, and picked it up on his way inside. Closing the door, he deposited the sack of clothes on the bed. "Sisters of Mercy have been by," he said to keep things light.

Abruptly Sue Ann ran across the room and flung her arms around his neck. He held her, silent for a moment. Then, stroking her back, he said, "There are consolidation loans, tax overhauls, agreements-in-principle with creditors—all kinds of ways to ease the financial bind on a company," he said. "In my heyday, I used to get pretty creative with such matters."

She sent him that grateful look he'd come to recognize. Then she tweaked his ear. "Go on, get out of here. I've got so much to get done today I don't know where to start."

He smiled. "You're incredible."

"No, just driven. I want us to have a home."

He tucked up the collar of the robe. "Me, too," he said. "The cabin—all that distance from town. When it's done, think what we can do with the extra time it'll take them to get to us."

Her eyes went soft. "I've got to call Laura, see if she's okay. And the relatives are flying home tomorrow. I want to see Serena before she leaves. Go on. Get out of here before I lose all sense of responsibility."

He laughed and went to find his boots and black ski jacket. Dressed and standing with the door open, he leaned in to kiss Sue Ann. "Say goodbye to everyone for me," he said. "Especially Serena. Meanwhile, I'll grab some breakfast rolls on my way out. You order a proper breakfast and take your time over it. Doctor's orders."

"Okay, Doc. I'll probably be at Laura's later today if you need to reach me."

He saluted, then closed the door.

SURROUNDED BY LEDGERS, tattered files and a yellow pad covered with calculations, Jerry was engrossed in the financial review of a business that had been poorly managed for years. Eric came in from the outer office, his hair looking wilder than before, and dumped yet another stack of files on the desk.

"The bank statements in there?" asked Jerry.

"Nope. Can't seem to find the bank stuff."

"No matter. I really don't need all this—" Jerry watched in frustration as three or four of the files slipped to the floor. Eric didn't notice, didn't stop. He was already headed back to the cabinets.

Jerry sighed, straightened, rubbed his lower back. He wasn't used to the desk work. Losing his touch—who wouldn't with a desperate company owner hovering over him, swamping him with cups of coffee, interrupting him with anecdotes about the good old days, showing him bulletins on mineral resources that hadn't the slightest bearing on the present mine contract.

Frazzled, Jerry glanced at the stained wall by the window. He angled his head to stare at a lopsided calendar: Miss January wore an ermine cape that didn't quite keep her safe from the cold. She'd hung crookedly on the wall for ten years, Jerry guessed. Like the window, the photo was yellowed with pipe tobacco and dust. He shook his head. The calendar said something about the shape of McMillan Survey—chaotic, inefficient, out-of-date.

The telephone rang. "I'll get it," he called, and picked up the black receiver. "McMillan Survey."

"How's it going?" Sue Ann responded, sounding hopeful. "Laura didn't want to bother you, but she's worried."

"Get Eric out of here," he said in a stage whisper, trying not to let his voice carry into the outer office. "He's a damned mother hen with the chicks missing. He's dragged out every file in the place, scattered them everywhere. Brought me sandwiches, coffee till I'm turning brown. I can't get anything done with his interruptions."

Instantly understanding, Sue Ann said, "Serena and I are going out to the cabin. We need a tough manly type to help us get up into the loft. Since you're busy, how about Eric?"

"Thanks, Sue Ann. Let me go get you a manly type. I'll call you back."

"What'll I tell Laura?"

Jerry explained that he'd already put in a call to Mel, outlined the dilemma, and asked the accountant to look around for a secretary as well as a firm that offered computerized bookkeeping services. If Eric would get out of his hair, he said, he'd call an attorney in L.A. who was an expert at contractual law, and see if anything could be done about the mine owner's implied responsibility for preserving the environment or covering the costs of preserving it.

"Can Eric afford all that?" Sue Ann asked.

"He'll have to. From what I've seen in the files, in letters of thanks and recommendations, he's respected in survey circles, so he's got money-making potential. But to pull his business out of the hole, he'll need to prove to a money man he has systems in place that will show he's improving his management structure. He'll need a loan."

After assuring Sue Ann he'd outline everything to Eric before committing him to major changes in the business, they hung up. His next task was to get Eric out of his hair. Rising from a maple chair whose chipped upright slats had probably scarred his back for life, he dodged piles of paperwork and went into the outer office.

He made it sound to Eric as if he'd take it as a personal favor if he'd go out to the cabin with Sue Ann. It was the truth, but the man balked. Jerry resorted to coercion.

"I don't want Sue Ann crawling around that burned-out shell alone," he said. "The floor's liable to give way under her or something. One of us has got to go."

Eric swept a hand through his hair. "I'd go, but you'll need me here. You're bound to have questions."

Jerry glanced meaningfully at the tornado of files and paperwork at his feet. "What I need is peace and quiet."

Eric glanced sheepishly at the mess he'd made.

"Look, man," said Jerry. "I know you've got a load to carry with this setback. But there are ways to ease things. Let me work on finding out what can be done. You've got to keep busy or you'll go crazy, so why not go on out to the cabin? If you'll give me a call here at about seven tonight, I'll fill you in on what you need to do to salvage your business."

For a second, Eric looked hopeful. "You mean it can be saved?"

"I think so, yes."

His brother-in-law took a step toward him, his gaze appreciative. "It would mean a lot. Laura and I have years of struggle packed into this company. I hate to think what it would do to us to lose it."

Jerry said gently, "I'll do what I can to rough things back together. Then you can step back in and see for yourself what an asset you've got here. It'll be a matter of tighter controls, utilizing the strengths of a few key personnel, and saving your energy for the things you do best. That's all company management is, really. Setting goals and using resources wisely. You've got the stuff for it, Eric."

Nodding, Eric looked distractedly at the dented gray file cabinet, evidently embarrassed. He put a proprietary hand on the top file drawer. "Teal," he said, not looking at Jerry. "Let me ask you something."

"What is it?"

"Accountants are like doctors, right?"

"In a way. Why?"

"I mean, they have a confidentiality with their clients." Eric seemed to force himself to look up. "Don't they?"

Jerry smiled at the thin veneer over Eric's pride. "Relax, Eric. You're as good as talking to a priest. Your secrets won't go beyond this room."

"Your word on it, Teal?"

"My word. Now how about giving Sue Ann a hand out at the cabin?"

Eric cast a last glance around the room. And, finally, he agreed to go.

Releasing his breath, rubbing his back, Jerry turned and headed toward the cluttered desk.

WHILE ERIC FLEW back to the mine site, supervised the dismantling of the camp and sold enough equipment to pay the crew half wages, Jerry worked in the office and began to see daylight. A week into the project, he arranged a preliminary meeting at the bank. Eric flew into town to attend it. Jerry brought in his personal financial statement, the bottom line of which caused the banker to raise his eyebrows, and then agreed to cosign on a five-year note that would finance Eric's comeback. However, the amount of the note hinged on the mine owner's responsibility for costs and environmental liability. Jerry had sent a copy of the contract to the Los Angeles attorney and was waiting for his opinion. In addition, Mel had recommended a secretary and she was due to begin work the following Monday. She would put the office in order and keep it that way. She'd also work with a local accounting firm to computerize the books.

On Friday of the second week, Eric came into the office for the mail—he wanted to review the mailing lists for upcoming contracts and select those for which he would bid. Even the two hours he was there proved tedious for Jerry, because Eric moved restlessly through the stacks of files, riffling them, repeatedly asking if Jerry had everything he needed.

Sue Ann came to Jerry's rescue again, as planned. In bed at night, wrapped in each other's arms and exhausted from their respective tasks, they compared notes on the progress they'd made, and in the mornings, like an old married couple—Sue Ann dressed in jeans and a sweatshirt and Jerry in slacks and a polo shirt—they went off to their projects, Sue Ann promising to run interference when she thought he might need it. And so it was on the day Eric came in for his mail. With uncanny intuition, Sue Ann called just as Jerry was about to demand Eric either get out of the office or salvage the business alone.

Chuckling at the irritation she heard in Jerry's voice when he got on the telephone, Sue Ann said, "Laura mentioned my brother was coming into the office this morning. Bad, is it?"

Jerry tossed his pencil to the desk. "You remember Papa Bear in 'Goldilocks?'"

"The grumpy one?"

"Right. That's what you'll have coming home to you tonight if we don't get him out of here."

"In that case—" She changed her voice, made it sound ultra-efficient. "Mr. Teal?"

"Yes?"

"This is Miss Matchett of Matchett Resources Inc., your friendly neighborhood head-hunting firm."

"Yes?" he said, beginning to grin. "How can I help you Miss—?"

"Matchett. We match needs to resources, Mr. Teal. We have a client looking for a strong manly type."

"Oh?"

"Yes, a type who won't mind acting as bodyguard to a lonely wife working with a wild and woolly construction crew at a remote cabin."

"If I weren't so tied up, I'd apply for the job myself, Miss Matchett. I have wonderful remedies for lonely wives."

"I'm certain you do, Mr. Teal, but this is strictly business. If you could send the man out, say, in half an hour?"

"Of course, Miss Matchett. And may I say, I look forward to our meeting this evening. I trust it won't be strictly business then?"

Laughing, she hung up.

Hearing her voice, her laughter, lifted Jerry's spirits. After nudging Eric out of the office without insulting him, Jerry went back to work feeling fresh and sharp.

It occurred to him that he missed using his skills in analysis and planning. Maybe he ought to take on a client or two, he mused; start a part-time financial-consulting business. Sue Ann had said she'd like to keep her management skills honed. Partnership... with his wife? Why not? Jerry smiled at the thought. It gave him a warm feeling in his gut. He'd talk it over with her tonight, see how she felt about the idea. They could still reserve time for priorities—traveling, exploring, making love.

The new dream inspired his work for Eric. He spent the afternoon reading handwritten notes, poorly typed statements and legal-looking documents, the collection of which formed the contractual agreements between McMillan Survey and its customers for the past ten years. He again skimmed through the mine contract, then phoned the attorney in L.A. who'd reviewed the case. Jerry learned that the owner of the mine was obligated to pay for the work Eric had completed—about half of the job. However, the owner would not have to pay for the unfinished work, the lawyer said, nor was he liable for costs related to environmental mishaps. Eric would have to eat the loss. It would hike up the bank loan by nearly one hundred thousand dollars.

It was going to be a hefty liability. Jerry wished for a moment that he could discuss the situation with Sue Ann. As cosigner he was, after all, liable for the bank note if Eric should default, and husbands and wives should discuss such things before leaping into them. But he'd given his word to keep the details of the business to himself, and after the first queries, Sue Ann had accepted the confidentiality without prying.

In fact, she had seemed cavalier about it. Her enthusiasm for the cabin reconstruction took priority over everything but making love, he thought. She'd been told that day that the stereo equipment badly needed cleaning and a few of the Plexiglas covers needed replacing, but that it was all working properly, and she was excited. "Couples can't tell each other everything," she'd joked with a glint in her eyes, when he'd referred again to the promise he'd made Eric. "What would be left to keep things exciting? I trust you to help Eric any way you can."

It had hiked up his ego a notch.

After talking with the attorney, Jerry realized his brother-in-law would be strapped. But with careful planning and a steady flow of work, McMillan Survey would pull through. Jerry decided he'd ask Eric for periodic meetings to monitor the financial end of the business. That should ensure Eric's ability to keep the company afloat.

Suddenly between tasks, Jerry grew aware of the thrum of car engines and occasional laughter from the street below. He glanced up. Weak lamplight poured through a window to his right. Getting up to stretch his legs, he went to the window and rubbed at the scum of pipe smoke and dust until he'd cleared away a blurry circle. He glanced down into the quaint downtown district.

The glow from turn-of-the-century lamps burnished the brick paving that accented Front Street, the lavenders, browns and reds of beautifully restored Victorian buildings fresh-looking from the moisture and clear air. The town obviously took pride in its history, he thought.

And then he wondered how Eric had managed to keep his office. There was probably a notice somewhere in the mass of papers, warning him to keep his windows clean.

Smiling wryly, Jerry was turning to return to the desk when he spotted a file on the floor, half the papers strewn around it. The file was marked Sue Ann. He bent, picked it up and began tapping the paperwork back inside. A McMillan Survey letterhead caught his eye. At this point it was habit to read anything related to the company, and Jerry automatically scanned the contents of the file.

"Need for absolute secrecy, Miss Blackburn," he read in a legal letter from Washington, D.C., addressed to Sue Ann.

And as he read, a great abyss opened in him, and through it poured disbelief, suspicion, and finally hurt that burned through him like lava.

He'd been used.

To receive a $50,000 legacy, Sue Ann had to be married by December 14. She and Jerry had been married November 15. In the file, a note from Eric to the attorney asked that the letter-of-trust be postmarked in Washington to preserve Eric's identity as benefactor. Jerry had read Sue Ann's ad in the *Times* on New Year's Day, two weeks after the date at the top of Eric's note—time enough for Sue Ann to receive the letter and place her ad. And he, Jerry, had been the convenient victim of her greed.

The pain of betrayal surged over him. Fighting through an unfamiliar mass of emotions, Jerry groped for the desk, the file slipping from his hands.

He'd sold his business, left his friends and destroyed his stable life—sacrificed everything—for a grasping, emotionally shaky manipulator. It stunned him that he'd been so wrong about her.

Confusion and distrust swirling through him, he recalled Sue Ann's capitulation that morning she'd thought he'd left the cabin without saying goodbye, and the memory sapped the strength from his legs. He swung around the desk and sat down. After weeks of playing cat-and-mouse sexually, she'd pressed that gorgeous naked body of hers against him as if he were water and she a woman dying of thirst. She had seemed really to feel something for him. So giving, so convincing, he thought, choked up again, sickened by his naiveté. Any man would have served her purpose.

He veered away from the emotional quagmire threatening to suck him down. He had to think, had to decide. Annulment? God, it hurt. Money, love, security—Sue Ann could have had it all, just by marrying him, if he'd never learned the truth.

Well, he had, hadn't he? He'd discovered he'd been suck-ered in by the epitome of what men feared in a woman—a conniving bitch. But she wouldn't get what she wanted. Eric, her secret benefactor, was broke.

Downstairs, a door slammed. He heard, as if through a voice-filter, Sue Ann calling out to him. And he grinned, but it was a grin stretched into a painful grimace. She would suf-fer, too.

Chapter Fourteen

As Sue Ann climbed the narrow staircase to Eric's office, she felt the muscles in her back tauten, and she paused to lean against the wall. Mental pressure or fatigue, she wondered. Probably both. None of the money she'd expected had arrived, and she'd been pouring everything she had into materials for the cabin. She'd been giving her all physically, too. At her urging, the construction crew had strung lights so they could work after dark, and tonight she'd labored in the bitter cold longer than she'd planned, hauling curtains, clothes and furniture out to the front porch where she sorted what could be cleaned and lugged the rest around back to a dumpster she'd rented. She sighed, unzipped her red parka and shook her head in dismay. She hadn't even taken time to shower away the soot, because by the time she'd gotten to town, it had been seven o'clock and Jerry would be more than ready to leave the office.

Now, as she forced one tired foot and then another up the stairs, she tried to phrase the difficult question she must ask her husband. *Will you lend me the money to outfit the kitchen, darling?* No, she couldn't say 'lend.' If she did, he'd want to know how she expected to pay him back, and she'd have to tell him about the legacy that had never arrived. The topic was off-limits until the money arrived—if it ever did.

Without the stress of saving McMillan Survey, Jerry might have gotten more involved in the financial end of reconstruction. But, pressed by his own responsibilities, he'd been easily deflected from the details by Sue Ann's vague responses to his questions and by her confident handling of the project. Now she had to have his help.

The insurance payoff was promised next week, but it wasn't enough to cover everything. She'd already dipped into her savings to cover cleaning and repair bills, an advance to the crew foreman, roofing materials, plus a few clothes and grooming aids for herself. With Jerry's wedding ring already paid for, that left her a few thousand to pay for Serena's last semester at college. Sue Ann was beginning to feel strung out. Jerry was her only alternative, and she tried again to gather the confidence to ask him for the money.

Pulling open the office door, she walked through neat stacks of file folders, trade magazines and technical manuals. Despite the fact that the materials weren't put away, the room reeked of organization. She could feel Jerry's presence all around her, and pride spread through her.

Yellow light pooled on the desk in the inner office. She could see Jerry's profile, slightly bent, his eyes intent on the ledgers. The sight warmed her, renewed her strength. The tiredness drained away. How unbelievable it was to love him, she thought, eager to feel his arms around her. He made her feel anchored in the good life.

"Miss Matchett here for our appointment, Mr. Teal," she said, coming around a stack of boxes and sliding her hand along his shoulder.

Jerry turned, and she bent down to hug him. For a moment, his arms closed around her, and then in a jerky movement he pulled away. Smiling, she stood up and looked into his face. And the smile faded.

Jerry's shadowed features looked haggard, the grooves deep around his mouth. Exhaustion—or something—made his eyes look lifeless.

"Darling," she said. "You're overworking. You look beat."

His mouth twisted strangely. When he spoke, his voice was rough. "You have charcoal on your chin."

Even as she brought up her hand to rub away the spot, her senses began to shimmer with foreboding. Something was wrong. Jerry looked ill. The work had obviously sapped his energy. And yet...something like tension made him seem stiff, unyielding.

"Jerry?" she said softly.

He turned away, began to line up pencils next to a tablet crosshatched with figures. "Yeah," he said. "I'm beat."

"Oh, me, too," she said, leaning over to rub his back. "How about room service, something really healthy like chicken, rice and salad, and then, right to sleep? We've been burning the candle at both ends, Jerry. We'll make ourselves sick."

His muscles remained rigid beneath her fingers. There was no give to him, no softness. How unlike the tender, physically responsive man who'd come home with her last night, thought Sue Ann.

Suddenly he shrugged off her hands, angled around her and went to the window to look outside at the nightlife. Her cheeks burning at the rebuff, she stared at his back.

He cleared his throat. "When did you decide to place that ad?" he said, his voice sounding muffled.

"You mean the one in the *Times*?"

"Yes, Sue Ann. The ad that brought me here."

Apprehension coiled through her. She fiddled with a corner of the yellow tablet, trying to figure what Jerry was driving at. Glancing at the rim-lighting on his dark hair and shoulders, she said finally, "Last December."

His shoulders seemed to slump, but she could have mistaken the movement. He braced himself against the window frame. "December?"

"Christmas," she added. "Why?"

"Who is Mark, Sue Ann?"

Off guard, she staggered against the chair. "Mark? He's...a man I used to know. Jerry, what is this?"

"That's what I'm trying to find out, Sue Ann. Just what you've set up here."

"Set up?"

"When you were distraught, out at the cabin, you muttered a name. Mark." Whirling, he took a step toward her. "Who the hell is he, Sue Ann?"

"An old lover," she shot back.

"Do you still see him?"

"No!"

"My God, Sue Ann. What did those scars on your arm do to your integrity so long ago?"

Automatically she grasped her arm. Hurt, anger and uncertainty waged a battle within, and she choked out, "What is this, Jerry? What happened to make you like this?"

The question seemed to check him. Abruptly, he turned, walked to the old *Playboy* calendar on the wall and straightened it. His fingers shook.

That spark of vulnerability urged her to move around the desk until she stood by his elbow. Forcing herself to recall Mark's dark-haired image and the old pain, she said, "Mark and I were engaged. He had lovers. There was an election coming up and the papers exploited his private life, ruined my reputation. I had a breakdown. I—"

Jerry angled a look at her. The heat of his gaze nearly took her confidence, it seemed so full of suspicion and hate. Had he met Mark in town? Found out Mark was behind the secret inheritance? The need to bridge the distance between them drove her past that wall of suspicion in his eyes, and into a tangle of emotion which left her feeling vulnerable. She tried to stick to the facts and keep talking.

"Mark worked for the governor, and I was just beginning to clerk in a government office. His position was precarious so we had to keep our relationship secret. After all, my cleaning houses on the side, trying to make ends meet, wasn't the proper image for a young political animal like Mark. The good jobs, back then, went to nurses and teachers. I had no training. It was rough."

"You think money's pretty important, then?"

Did he know about the legacy? "I—yes. Yes, money has been important since my first husband died and I had a baby to support. Do you understand that, Jerry? Or has it always been a breeze for you? Making money. Living the good life."

"Yeah," he said sarcastically, "I've always lived good."

"You're lucky. But I thought you knew, money isn't what's really important in life."

He laughed in evident disbelief. "No? What is important, Sue Ann? Relationships?"

"Yes."

"I see."

"What exactly do you see, Jerry? You're giving me the third degree. What do you want to know about? Mark? My ex-lovers? Is it jealousy at this late date?"

He grinned with that knife-edged sarcasm, and didn't answer.

The secret of the legacy begged to be told, but she was afraid. "Do you want me to make an accounting of my finances?" she asked, her nails biting into her palms. "You should have done that before the prenuptial was drawn up."

His gaze burned in bitterness. "I should have done a lot of things before the prenuptial was drawn up. But you made damned sure nobody but you was doing the thinking, didn't you, Sue Ann?"

She stepped back, turned away, the hurt crushing her. "My God," she breathed. "What's happening to us?"

"You mean to say you care?"

She whirled. "Yes, I—" The words of love stuck in her throat. There had never been time to say them. In the back of her mind was the notion she'd tell him on their first night in the cabin, but that date loomed far in the future. And right now his coldness choked the life out of her feelings of love.

"Go on," he prodded. "Let me hear how much you care, Sue Ann."

"I care," she whispered, clenching her fists. "Damn you, I care!"

He laughed out loud and walked away. Picking his ski jacket off a box, he slipped his arms into the sleeves and flipped up the collar.

Sue Ann fought back tears. They were actually fighting. He was being cruel. She must find out what was wrong. Had the shambles of Eric's business given Jerry second thoughts about marrying her? Had Mel mentioned that she'd asked if Mark had been in touch lately? It could be anything... *Anything, Dear God, but the inheritance.*

Her fatigue made it difficult to think, but Sue Ann refused to give in to the fear that washed her limbs and left them weak. Straightening her shoulders, she said, "Jerry, we can't leave things like this, just go back to the hotel as if nothing's between us. Please tell me what's wrong."

"It can be said in one sentence. I want an annulment."

"What?" A blackness surged up around Sue Ann. Her legs turned molten, and she groped, found the wall.

"That might not fit with your plans," he was saying in that distant flat voice, while she began to shake violently. "But then, you never really considered what I wanted, anyway."

"Never considered?"

"Never."

It took effort to clasp her hands for control, turn her head and look at him. His silhouette, against the lamplight, was blurry. "What . . . did you . . . ?"

"What would I have wanted, had you asked?" He leaned against the desk, ticked off items on his fingers. "A couple of people on my side of the church, for one."

An involuntary gasp burst from her. She'd never really pressed him for the names and addresses of people he might want to invite. How horrible. How thoughtless.

She was forming an apology when he chuckled mirthlessly. "Perhaps it was an oversight. Whatever. There's still our honeymoon. You didn't give a damn that I wanted to go south, to the islands. You had to go back to your precious cabin."

"Ours," she whispered.

"What?"

"Our precious cabin. I would have gone with you, though, had I known what it meant to you."

"I tried to tell you. As usual, you didn't listen. But that's water under the bridge. It's probably better we stayed here. Look how much you've already gotten done on the reconstruction."

"I can't do much more," she said, knowing it wouldn't matter now how she said it. "I'm almost out of money."

"Running a little short, are we, love? I'll leave a nice chunk of money in the bank for you." He glanced at the desk. "And I'll write down final instructions on McMillan Survey for Eric tonight at the hotel. Least I can do, him finally approving of me the way he has."

"Eric just took a while to appreciate you." The desperation thick in her voice, she cleared her throat. "He was concerned for my happiness."

"Everyone, it seems, is concerned for your happiness, Sue Ann. To hell with anyone else's."

She stepped toward him, stood with her hands clenched at her side. "That's not true!"

"Isn't it? I fill a purpose for you people, that's all. Anyone would do. Give the groom a face and a body, tell him to be here on time, and marry him, isn't that the way it went, Sue Ann? Just as planned? What did you do with that collection of applications for your ad—draw my name from a hat?"

Anger shoved in under her desperation, like a sliver under a fingernail. "Obviously Eric had good reason to be skeptical about you. You're heartless."

"Yeah," he said. "Heartless because I saw the light about you before it was too late."

"The 'light' being?"

"You're a conniving—" His jaw rigid, he added, "It's your plans that're important to you, Sue Ann. Not mine. It's too bad they no longer include me."

"*My* plans?" She went to him and, heedless of his reaction, gripped the front of his coat. "What about your plans? You had a few of your own steeped in hidden motive. Trying to buy me off from the start with money and precious gifts— what was behind it, Jerry? And for that matter, what would you have done if I'd refused to sign the prenuptial? That was awfully calculating of you, bringing a blank prenuptial up here with you and springing it on me."

His face deepened in hue, and his eyes blazed. "I'm amazed it didn't throw you off-track. You just signed it and kept right on bulldozing your way through the wedding plans. But then, you did that about my suggestion to expand the kitchen and dining area at the cabin, too. A real field general, you are."

She only just kept from biting her lip in humiliation. "My 'plans' didn't include living with someone like you," she snapped. "A good-time Charlie who has no sense of responsibility and commitment."

He grabbed her arms, nearly lifting her off the floor.

No man had ever laid violent hands on her. The fact that Jerry looked as if he'd crush her if he could spurred her fury. "Go on, get an annulment. It's better I see this side of you now than spend a lifetime in your miserable company."

His gaze riveted her. A familiar current arced through her, and her lids trembled. For a moment she thought she saw something soften him—a memory, a longing—God, she felt it, too. But she misjudged him. He loosened his hands, set her roughly back from him.

"My feelings exactly." He tipped a hand to his temple. "My attorney will be in touch."

Before she could grasp that it was really over, Jerry turned, scooped up the yellow tablet and walked out.

THE SUBARU SKIDDED wide on the left turn just past the Juneau/Douglas Bridge. Buried in self-recriminations and emotional pain and only half-aware of what she was doing, Sue Ann felt that quick jolt of adrenaline that comes a hair's breadth before catastrophe, and she jerked the steering wheel to the left. The car snaked, skittered sideways along the icy Douglas Highway. Her heart hammering, she nudged the wheel to correct the slide. The car began to whip around. She gave it gas, drove into the spin and took up the slack, the milliseconds of trying to bring the car under control seeming like hours. Then, as the vehicle came around a third time, she misjudged her speed and stood on the brake. The car slid across the road and rammed into the snowbank. Metal crunched against frozen snow. The safety harness bit into Sue Ann's shoulder as she rocked with the impact. The engine died, and the right wheel crept up over the bank and spun.

Sue Ann's control shattered. The emotions she'd held in check throughout the fight with Jerry and during her instinctive flight to Douglas were suddenly unleashed by the accident. With a wail of despair, she fell against the wheel and wept. Her shoulders shook, and her eyes brimmed with the effort her body made to cleanse itself of the dust of her life.

All her plans. All she'd worked for. Everything in shambles—her husband estranged, her home destroyed, her car dented and impaled on a snowbank, and her falling to pieces on the shoulder of a dark icy road.

Her alienation was total, and she felt old. Forty years was a long time to struggle, she thought. Gripping the steering wheel, she grimaced out at the blur of yellow light her headlights made on the steep bank in front of the car. Life was so damned hard. What could she do this time to pull herself back from the darkness? What plan could she throw together that would hold water?

Nothing, she felt. The man she'd married was a stranger, and with a hatefulness she'd never encountered before in a mate, he'd thrown her organizational skills in her face. It left her without confidence. She felt inadequate, empty, devoid of value.

That brought fresh tears, and she thought: the worst of it was, some of what he'd said was true. She *had* ignored Jerry's needs. Even now, as she bit down on her lip to stop crying, her face reddened at the knowledge that, of all the hundreds of people he must have known before coming to Juneau, he'd only had Clint with him at the wedding. What did he care that the Attorney General of Alaska had attended the reception? He'd probably rather have seen a hunting or golfing buddy, or even a distant cousin, sampling the smoked salmon. Oh, she'd made a mess of things. She'd organized him right out of her life.

But what had prompted the breakup? And how would she bring him back? Whatever had broken his faith in her was bad, very bad, and if she thought telling him about the secret legacy would mend things, she'd do it, she vowed. But it wasn't the legacy. If he'd known about the money, he'd have confronted her with it. Since he hadn't, she couldn't make things worse by telling him.

There had been too much stress in her life, she mused in distraction, rifling her purse for a tissue and mopping her eyes. The familiar warning signs of breakdown hovered. The blackness. The despair. The sense of aloneness.

How easy it would be to slip into mental oblivion, as she had after losing Mark, as she nearly had after the fire. Just let the darkness take over and the world keep churning away on the other side of the curtain. She longed to go to the cabin to rest and gather her strength. The memory of its solitude beckoned. But she couldn't go there; it was an alien place—charred, torn up, littered with Skilsaws and heavy-duty electrical cords and lumber.

Ah, God, she prayed, *oblivion isn't the answer, is it? Because if I gave up now, I'd lose him permanently. Jerry was good enough to fight for. But how? Where were the answers?*

She wanted Serena, wanted the levelheaded wisdom of her daughter—*It's people that count. Not things. A ring is just a ring, Mama*—but Serena was back at school. *Who is left?* Sue Ann wondered.

An image of lobster-red hands and wry abruptness laced with brotherly love made her sit up and reach for the keys swinging in the ignition. She had to talk to Eric. Besides herself, her brother was the only person with whom Jerry had spent any time these past two weeks. Eric would know what had set Jerry against her.

Unfastening her seatbelt, she flicked the key and the electric starter hummed. But the engine refused to turn over. For ten minutes she tried unsuccessfully to start the car. When at last it was evident something crucial had broken loose in the engine when she'd struck the snowbank, she sighed and turned off the headlights. Zipping up her jacket, she collected her purse and climbed out into the twenty-degree air.

Already her mind was clicking through her alternatives. Gas station. Tow truck. Back down the road half a mile, the bridge arched across to the boat harbors and docks of waterfront Juneau. From the Douglas side of the bridge, she knew she could look past Gastineau Channel to the Breakwater Inn. The thought cramped up her heart, and she shut her eyes at the image of Jerry, sitting at the table in the upper corner room, the lamplight flooding over his shoulder as he made notes about salvaging Eric's business. That is, she corrected, a light would be shining from the room if Jerry had gotten a taxi to take him directly back to the hotel after their—

She spun around and started up the road, toward lights that twinkled between hills and trees, her breath puffing in silver clouds. She'd actually been thinking of going back to talk to Jerry. But she couldn't go back until she had a clue to what had made him behave as if she had been a scorpion poised to strike him. If she went back unarmed and they fought again, he might simply pack his things and leave town. It was too horrible to contemplate.

Striding purposefully uphill, ignoring the strain in her tired muscles, she considered the alternatives. She could hike across the bridge to the gas station and get a tow, but that would cost her an hour or more, because they'd want her to come back with the car. Talking with Eric was a priority.

She glanced up the road. The lights of homes glittered like stars among the black spikes of trees and the grays of moonlit snow-covered hills. It was still early, maybe eight-thirty. She would knock on a door, she decided; ask for a lift to Eric's, where she'd call for a tow truck and talk to her brother while she waited for the car to be repaired. Then she'd go back to Jerry.

The idea of their reunion inspired her. As she trudged along, she shied away from hopelessness, held fast to the knowledge that she was a veteran planner. Like two sides of a coin, Viv had once told her, a person's strength was also her weakness. Well, she was operating from the strong side of her nature now—but wiser, humbler, smarter. She'd be better at planning than she'd ever been before. She had to be, because her marriage was at stake, and she was going to pull it back together.

SHE'D LET HERSELF into the McMillan home hours ago, only to find that the family wasn't home. Laura had mentioned dropping Tana at a friend's house for a slumber party, but somehow Sue Ann must have missed an explanation of how Laura and Eric planned to spend the evening. After calling Mike's Place and Louie's, the two spots her brother and Laura were most likely to be found if they were out on the town, she learned the couple had been in for dinner and cocktails, and had left for Juneau.

Sue Ann knew Laura was behind the night out; her sister-in-law was wisely taking Eric's mind off the pitiful state of his company. It was the kind of thing Laura was good at—softening the punches life occasionally threw at Eric—and it made Sue Ann miss Jerry the more.

As she waited, knowing the station had repaired her car and that she couldn't get a ride back to it until Eric came home, her tension increased. She paced, played some of Eric's old Creedence tapes, made herself a toddy and drank it. Still she waited, and still the couple didn't return home.

At midnight, she grew possessed of the idea she must talk to Jerry. For half an hour she sat on a stool at the breakfast bar and stared at the telephone on the wall. Call him or wait? Call. No, she decided; without some insight into his anger, it might be worse to talk to him now. And yet the feeling that time was of the essence gnawed at her patience. She felt she must talk to him.

Her mouth went dry. Her hand trembled. Gingerly she picked up the receiver and dialed the hotel. The desk rang the room. The signal chattered eight times. She hung up, waited twenty minutes, then dialed again. Still no answer.

I like to have a good time, he'd said so often. Perhaps he'd gone out somewhere with Mel or one of the other guys he knew. Maybe he'd gone back to Eric's office. Hopeful again, she dialed, but the chattering of the summons went unanswered.

Tears threatened. Abruptly she rose from the breakfast bar and went down into the living room, to the couch, where she crawled beneath an orange-and-brown afghan and closed her eyes. To ease the pain in her heart and relax her body, she resorted to breathing exercises. She would need her strength for this campaign, she told herself, exhaling. She was a field general; Jerry had called her that when he was angry and had meant it as an insult, but it was true. She was. Even field generals took a nap between battles. Otherwise they had nothing left when the next battle was pitched.

She calmed herself by dint of will and slept.

"WHAT'S THIS? Sleeping Beauty and no prince? What're you doing here, Sue Ann?"

The growl was Eric's voice. Sue Ann blinked and sat up. She brushed her hair out of her face. "Eric. Laura. What time is it?"

Her blue peacoat open and her blouse buttoned awry, as if she and Eric had been parked somewhere like teenagers and had come home to be more comfortable, Laura hung onto Eric's arm. She stared at Sue Ann, her features cramped in a frown.

Eric's arm was around his wife, and he squeezed her close so he could peer down at his watch. "It's six o'clock. How come you're here?"

"Jerry and I—we—" Sue Ann rubbed her face, trying to put the momentous fact of the breakup into words "—we had a fight. I need to talk to you, Eric."

"Sure, but Laura and I have been playing cards at Mel's most of the night. I'm beat."

"Was he there?" Sue Ann rose from the couch, her gaze eager. "Jerry?"

"No. I've got a meeting with him and the bank at eleven, though. I need some sleep."

Laura jabbed him in the ribs.

Eric glanced at her. "What?"

"She's in trouble," said Laura. "I'll put the coffee on."

Twisting out of his embrace, Laura turned toward the kitchen.

Sue Ann felt creaky and blue. "Let me just wash up," she said to Eric, and hurried up the steps and down the hall.

When she'd freshened up and she and Eric were sitting at the breakfast bar, sipping coffee, Laura set bacon and eggs opposite them on the counter beside the range. She dropped four slices of bread into the toaster.

Watching his wife, Eric said, "Start at the beginning, Sue Ann. What started the fight?"

"That's just it," said Sue Ann, worrying her lip. "I don't know. I thought maybe he'd said something to you."

"Not a word. He was always damned glad to see my back-side going out the door—it put him in good spirits every time he managed to get me out of the office. But besides that, he's been easy to be around. He's a damned good guy, Sue Ann."

"I know."

"I was wrong about him." Eric looked down at his hands, wrapped around the mug. It was close to an apology.

Sue Ann touched the sleeve of his blue plaid shirt. "You were rough on him. But I know you were thinking of me, and I told him that last night."

His head came up. "He mentioned it? My being hard on him?"

She nodded. "He's a fair man. When he's not angry, he'll understand why."

Eric grimaced. "If I caused any problems between you, why I-I'd—"

Sue Ann saved him the discomfort of finishing. "It's not you, it's me. I didn't consider his needs." Remembering Jerry's accusations choked her up, but she pressed through, hoping Eric would think of some reason for the change in her husband. "He said I was conniving."

Eric's head came around. "What did he mean?"

"I don't know. Maybe that I was selfish, planning everything my way. I didn't even ask Jerry if he wanted his friends to come to the wedding."

Eric studied her a moment. "Well, you do have that in you."

Sue Ann swallowed. "I felt I had to."

"Why? You never stop to think that what you want isn't right for everyone else."

That hurt her, and she took a quick sip of coffee; the hot liquid burned her tongue, her throat, and the heat was a welcome diversion. "We've established my faults," she said wryly.

"Okay, okay," said Eric. "But when Jerry agreed to help me with the business, where were you when he came home exhausted at night?"

Laura's head jerked up. "Eric!"

"Well, it's true," Eric said, snatching his pipe from his pocket and waving it at his wife. "You know good and well we discussed it, Laura."

"But she's been through enough. Leave her alone."

"I won't leave her alone." He angled a hard look at Sue Ann. "When are you going to stop thinking you're the only one with problems in this world?"

Sue Ann stood up. "I never felt that way!"

"Bull! You're so locked into 'poor Sue Ann' you don't even know when other people are hurting. If Laura had been as self-indulgent as you all these years, do you think I'd have stuck with her?"

Sue Ann glanced at Laura. "Do you think I'm totally without feeling for others, Laura?"

Her cheeks pink, Laura ducked her head to be sure the toast didn't burn.

"Am I?" demanded Sue Ann, her heart in her throat.

Laura finally met Sue Ann's penetrating gaze. "I think you're the best sister-in-law anyone could ever have," she said. "You're so accomplished and spirited and warm, who wouldn't love you? Tana adores you. So many people do, Sue Ann." She sent a hot look at Eric. "Even your brother, though sometimes you could never tell it, he's so rough on you." The woman's gaze swept back to Sue Ann. "You're both rough on those you love the most. I've always wondered why."

Sue Ann studied the flush on Eric's cheeks. "Why *are* we so hard on each other?"

He stuck his pipe in his mouth, talked around it while he pawed his shirt for matches. Laura tossed him a pack. He lit up. The smoke curled around him, hazing his eyes as he narrowed them on Sue Ann. "Our parents," he was saying. "They taught us. Family comes first."

"Of course it does."

"The old man gave us everything. Remember?"

"Of course."

"Life was a snap when we were growing up, wasn't it?"

"Life was just about perfect. We had everything."

"And then nothing."

Suddenly Sue Ann knew what he was driving at. She sat down. "Just—" she looked at him "—us."

He poked the pipe stem at her. "Bingo. And the first time life threw you a punch, you know, with Bill, it scared the day-lights out of you."

She knew what was coming, and felt her stomach turn over. She put out her hand. "Eric—"

"You couldn't take it when life got tough, Sue Ann."

"Eric, please—"

He grasped her scarred arm, instantly riveting her attention on him. "Don't you think I understood? At least I got to hear Dad's lectures on being a man, being responsible, looking out for the womenfolk. You got nothing but pretty clothes and plenty of time to daydream. When life threw punches, you had nothing to fight them."

Tears stung her eyes. "I tried. I worked—oh, how I worked to keep things safe for me and Serena."

He shook her arm. "I watched you. What do you think it did to me, seeing you claw and scrape to survive? You fell apart when you lost Mark, and I blamed myself for not making you see what he was. Then you buried yourself out at that cabin. I had to sit by and watch you waste your life."

They looked at each other, the years suddenly capsulized in this moment, and suddenly they were holding each other. Sue Ann hugged him hard and whispered, "Eric, I love you."

"Me, too," came his rasped reply.

"Don't you see," she said. "I couldn't lose again. It was so important to do everything right with Jerry. Control all the circumstances, make it come out right."

The comment seemed to make him uncomfortable. Looking away, he set her back on the stool. "You can't do it like that, Sue Ann." He glanced at Laura, who stared at them with tears in her eyes. He gestured, "Honey . . . ?"

Laura came around to Sue Ann. "What he means is, you've got to do the best you can in life and then just relax and enjoy it." Laura straightened Sue Ann's hair, smiled at her. "You've got to trust the man upstairs to ease the load. And you've got to trust your loved ones to be there for you when you can't do any more. Eric means to say, trust and love keep the bad things at bay." She looked across Sue Ann's shoulder to Eric, the love palpable. "The thing that makes life bearable is love."

Sue Ann turned away from Laura's face, the longing for Jerry slicing like a hot knife through her heart. "How will I get him back?" she murmured.

Laura patted her shoulder. "Trust him enough to tell you what's wrong."

"But if I just had a clue. He said something about Mark. Was I seeing him again? Of all the ridiculous notions. Eric, had you mentioned Mark to Jerry?"

Abruptly, Eric got up and went down into the living room.

Her whole being coming alive with premonition, Sue Ann slid around Laura and followed him. She stood rigidly beside Eric as he studied the gray skies, her heart beginning to thrum. "Eric, what did you say to Jerry? Tell me."

"It's . . . not Mark. I don't know anything about Mark."

"Then, what? For the love of God, *what*?"

Eric turned, and Sue Ann saw anguish stretch his features. "Sue Ann," he said, grasping her shoulders, "it was for your own good. I didn't ever mean to meddle."

"Meddle in what, Eric?"

"Your private life." His fingers pressed into her. "But you were wasting it!"

"Damn you," she said, jerking away. "What have you done? Tell me!"

"A letter. I sent you a letter."

"I got no letter, Eric."

His eyes widened. "No letter from Washington? You mean, it never came?"

Realization bolted through her. "The legacy," she said under her breath, looking at Eric with incredulity. "You told him about it."

"Then you got it?"

"Ah, God, *why* did you tell him?" she moaned, clenching her hands. "Everything's ruined. He'll never trust me, now."

Laura came down to them, hurrying to put her arm around Sue Ann. "Eric? What's this about a letter?"

Eric's face jerked in awkward angles as he looked from his wife to his sister. He gestured, seeming to want to explain, but said nothing.

The two women stared at him. Laura said quietly, "Tell us about the letter, sweetheart."

He walked to the gun cabinet.

Sue Ann stepped away from Laura. "So it was you, Eric. You sent the letter!"

Anger making her movements snappy, she collected her purse and jacket from a corner chair. "I can tell you about it," she said to Laura, poking her arms into the sleeves. "He ignored the fact that you've been scraping to get by for years. On the basis of his first big contract, he promised to give me $50,000—if I married by December 14."

Laura drew in a breath.

"Yes," said Sue Ann. "How's that for attempted manipulation? Then he gave the man I chose absolute hell because he thought I'd chosen the wrong man. Isn't that right, Eric?"

"Jerry must have found the file," her brother said, thinking out loud, his face turned away.

"What file?" said Sue Ann, coming to him. "Eric, dammit, what file?"

Eric faced around, looking distracted. "The file I kept in the office. I kept going back to try to find it, but I never did."

Sue Ann's insides shook. "What was in the file?"

"A copy of the trust agreement. Jerry must have read it." Eric swore, but Sue Ann barely heard.

She tugged on his arm. "You've got to give me a ride. Now, hurry. I've got the awful feeling Jerry thinks—oh, never mind, just give me a ride to the hotel. There's no time to hassle with my car."

Without asking questions, Eric grabbed his coat and Laura turned off the coffeepot. The three of them piled into Eric's pickup and headed out of Douglas.

"And to think you tried to make me feel guilty about being a marine corps sargeant," Sue Ann said, leaning around Laura to glare at Eric. "Well, I'll tell you something, Eric. I am one. It gets me through life, and I'm damned well not going to change because it bothers you."

Eric glanced at her, his eyes pleading. "It was Dad," he said. "We learned it from Dad."

"You accused me of being like him, as if it was a sin, when you are yourself a worrywart and a manipulator."

"I know, I know, and I'm sorry. It's not a trait I like in anyone, least of all myself. Laura's done her best to shave the edge off the worst of it." He smiled gravely at his wife. "Laura, I should have discussed the money with you before extending myself the way I did. I wanted to so many times. Especially when we lost the mine contract. I let everyone down."

Laura squeezed his thigh, and it made Sue Ann close her eyes to think she might have lost the right to that little intimacy with the best man she'd ever known.

The thought of Jerry softened her anger. "Oh, Eric," she said, frowning. "I appreciate your good intentions, but you could have told me when you lost that contract it was you who set up the legacy. I would have understood. It would have saved us all so much misery."

"I wanted to tell you when I came over to the hotel that day, when I asked Jerry to help me. But I couldn't face it. I'd let you down. Forced you to get married before you were ready."

Sue Ann's head came around. "Is that what you think?"

"Yeah." He shrugged, looking exhausted. "I mean, it was obvious. You hadn't made any moves on your own. Then you put that ad together, and I felt awful."

"You thought I'd done that because of the money?"

"Well . . . yeah."

She sighed. "Oh, Eric. You're wrong. And Jerry's wrong."

Again the premonition that time was speeding away from her made her clench her hands. It was an eternity before Eric pulled into the parking lot behind the Breakwater and let her out, saying he'd cancel the appointment with the bank and wait in the car in case Jerry wanted corroboration for her explanations.

Fumbling for the key to the motel-room door, Sue Ann finally got it open and flew into the room. "Jerry?" she called, not seeing him in the main room. No one answered, and a cold panic settled on her when she saw that his trunks and suitcases were gone. The rose-patterned vase gleamed beside the telephone—symbol of the catastrophes that had marred her marriage. Swallowing around a feeling of loss, Sue Ann turned away.

Where were the notes for Eric? Spotting the paperwork on the table, she rushed to look at it.

Sue Ann,
Please tell Eric I won't be able to make the meeting with the bank. I'll be in touch tomorrow about where the papers can be sent. With certain provisions I outlined in the note for Eric, I'll still back him. Just tell him that. He'll know what I'm referring to. Thinking it over, I can appreciate how your secret deal wasn't entirely your fault. You were enticed by someone who meant well. But when it came to something as important as marriage, Sue Ann, you should have stuck to your scruples. Love can't be bought. And love is, after all, what makes life good. I'm deeply sorry it couldn't be for us. My attorney will send you the money I mentioned last night. Please direct any questions you might have to him. He'll know where to reach me.

Jerry

It was long seconds before Sue Ann realized the words were blurring. Gone. Jerry was gone. He wasn't giving her any opportunity to hear that she'd learned to listen to his needs, and that she would face life trusting him to be her partner.

She heard a sound behind her, and was turning, hoping Jerry had changed his mind and come back, when Eric barged into the room. "I thought I'd better explain," he was saying, looking around for Jerry.

"He's gone!" Sue Ann crumpled the note.

"What do you mean, gone?" asked Eric, checking the room for Jerry. "He can't be gone."

"His clothes are gone, he's gone!"

Eric glanced at his watch. "He's probably taking the seven-forty flight. No time to catch him."

Sue Ann started. "What time is it?"

"Twenty after."

Abruptly, Sue Ann picked up the telephone and asked the desk to connect her to the airport. "You've got to page him," she said when they answered. "Jerry Teal. Say it's an emergency."

She waited, barely able to swallow. She gave Eric his notes. He scanned them and paced, running a hand through his hair and glancing at his watch.

Then Jerry's voice came across the line, sounding rough from lack of sleep. "This is Jerry Teal. What's the emergency?"

"Matchett Resources here," she croaked. "We match resources to needs, and we've got a woman desperate to find a husband who's leaving without knowing the truth about her love."

A long silence. "It's too late, Sue Ann. Your love can be bought, and they're calling my flight. See you—"

"No! Jerry, Eric's here. He'll tell you. I didn't marry you for the money."

"How would he know, Sue Ann? Look, I'm not really cut out for marriage anyway. All this emotional stuff wears me down. I can't seem to cope with it. Let's just say it didn't work for either of us. Final call. I've got to go."

"Please listen, Jerry. I've got proof that I got the idea to place the ad before Eric sent me that letter from Washington. Just delay your flight till two o'clock, and if I don't convince you it wasn't the money that made me choose you, I won't say

anything about your leaving. Because if there can't be trust
between us from now on, the marriage will never work. Jerry?
Will you hear me out?''

In the background, two flights were announced before he
answered. "All right, Sue Ann. I'll be in the lobby."

She was shaking when she hung up. "He's waiting," she said
to Eric. "I need a ride to the cabin and then to the airport."

"Let's go," said Eric, ushering her out the door.

In a little over an hour, the proof tucked into the pocket of
her parka, a package tucked under her arm—and her family
waiting as backup in the parking lot—Sue Ann pushed
through the doors at the airport. She scouted the waiting
room, looking for the tall figure she'd met here just over two
months ago and had grown to love.

He came up on her left side. Ironically, he was wearing the
same gray sport coat and gray-green tie he'd worn the night he
arrived, the colors that made his eyes seem deep as a still lake.
"Looking for me?" he said neutrally.

She looked into his face and saw exhaustion etched in the
deep lines. "Oh, yes," she said, a poignant ache softening her
voice. "You won't be sorry you missed that flight."

"Why don't we let me decide that?"

"All right."

He took her elbow and directed her to a dim corner away
from the crowds. She set the package she'd brought him in the
corner and turned around.

"You were right about the cabin," she said, trembling. "The
kitchen and dining areas are too cramped. I just looked, not
half an hour ago. The northwest wall should go out about six
feet."

"Sue Ann, that's premature. We haven't agreed—"

"Yes, of course." Reaching into her pocket, she drew out a
folded scrap of newsprint. Her fingers shook so violently she
had difficulty opening it.

Jerry touched her hand. "Take it easy," he said. Neither the
tone nor the touch was intimate, but the memory of his saying those words to her at Skater's Cabin branded her like hot
wire.

"This is just so important," she said, trying to flatten out
the news clipping.

"What have you got there?" he asked, almost too coolly, and it sounded as if he might be hiding his own churning emotions.

"A Personals column," she said, taking heart from the thought he still cared. "It's the proof I wanted to show you."

"Where did you get it?"

"From the paper, Christmas morning. I got the idea to put my own ad in the *Times* from reading this. See, Jerry? The date is December 25." She held it up. "Days before I received Eric's letter from that attorney in Washington."

"Sue Ann," he chided. "Eric received his approval copy early in December."

"But..." Rummaging in her pocket, she pulled out the envelope from Washington. It was blackened at one corner, where the return address should have been. "The postmark," she said, showing it to him. "It's December 28. I didn't get this letter until the second of January."

Jerry studied the envelope, skepticism and something closer to hope changing his features from one split second to the next.

"Jerry," she said, "it wasn't the letter from Washington that made me decide to place that ad. On Christmas Day, with Eric and Laura gone to Hawaii and Serena at school, I finally realized I didn't want to be alone anymore. The cabin was empty. I wanted someone to share it with me. That letter didn't arrive until after I'd called in my ad. I promise you that."

"Sue Ann, I want to believe you."

"Listen to this, then." Flattening out the clipping, she read, "'Wanted: Sensitive, intelligent, loving mate. Must enjoy outdoors, reading, music, quiet chats by the fireplace.' You see, I copied my ad so exactly from snippets of this column that I put in fireplace instead of stove. Don't you remember the mistake? And look at this," she said, showing him underlined phrases from several ads. "'I'm professional, goal-oriented, attractive, loyal and loving.' I copied all that, but it's the truth. Then I put in something on my own about wanting to share the beauty of—"

"'Alaska with an adventuresome, fun-loving reliable man looking to marry a choosy woman of the North,'" Jerry finished for her.

She looked up, and the warmth and regret she saw in his eyes made her grasp his arm for support.

" 'Send letter with photo,' " they said together, as solemnly as wedding vows.

"You remember the exact words," she said in awe.

"I crammed before the test." His face breaking into a smile, he reached into the inside pocket of his suit and pulled out a clipping. "I've been reading and rereading it, trying to figure how I could have been so wrong about you. And wondering how much of a fool I was being, not to stick it out with you anyway."

"Then you believe me?"

He tucked the clipping away, a smile lighting up his face. "What was it you wanted me to believe, Sue Ann?"

She slipped the evidence into her pocket, stepped up close to his chest and put her heart in her eyes when she gazed at him. "Believe that I love you," she said.

"Oh, Sourdough . . ."

She couldn't resist. " 'Oh, Sourdough,' " she mimicked.

His eyes crinkled in amusement. He caressed her hair. He took her jaw in his hands and slowly lowered his mouth to hers. The kiss explored that frail link of trust connecting them, and was the more tender for the tenuousness of their relationship. Sue Ann's head relaxed in his hands. Jerry moved her gently to the rhythm of his kiss, and she began to forget that fishermen and families and woodsmen in backpacks milled around only a few yards from their darkened corner. She wrapped her arms around Jerry's back, melting against him, responding to his kiss with her own creative exploration of his mouth. Somehow he freed his lips from hers and ran his mouth along her throat to the warm curve of shoulder beneath her coat and blouse. "More feeling this time," he commanded. "Say it."

She knew what he wanted, because the moan was nearly to her lips. As he pulled away her collar and kissed the sensitive flesh above her breast, she murmured, "I love you."

"Sue Ann. I nearly lost the chance to hear you say that."

Pulling back, she searched his features. "What if this kind of misunderstanding happens again, Jerry? You were running out on me without trying to work things out. Our marriage will never survive if we run from our problems.''

He frowned. ''I was afraid to trust you, Sue Ann. Afraid to trust my feelings about you. I was so afraid that I moved out of our room last night, in case you came back, and stayed in another hotel.''

''At midnight,'' she mused. ''I felt it.''

He nodded. ''All night long, and coming out to the airport, I was smothered in guilt. I knew I was running out on you. I felt you'd betrayed me, and I used that to make it easy to run.''

''Why? Why did you want to run, Jerry?''

He glanced over his shoulder at the crowds. ''You see those people?''

Looking, she said she did.

''Every one of them has a story, Sue Ann. Lost children, broken hearts. A mother dying of cancer...''

Sue Ann took his arm.

''I thought that by keeping things light,'' he continued, ''I wouldn't have to hear any more of those stories, get mixed up in any more painful emotions. Sue Ann, running from people's problems has been a way of life for me since my mom fell ill. As I mentioned before, my mom raised me alone. She was independent, but she was also highly emotional—strung out, I'd even say. She couldn't handle pressure, loneliness, so many things. So I filled the support role a husband would have done. You know, entertained her with jokes, played cards and traveled with her, discussed leaky sinks with plumbers, that kind of thing. When she got sick, I took care of her for years, really loved her and looked after her. She died anyway, and I felt I hadn't given enough—or maybe too much. Anyway, there was nothing left to give. Not to my ex-wife, nor to you. And you were needy. I saw that at Skater's Cabin, and at the wedding, and again when the cabin burned.''

He took a breath and plunged on. ''So when I thought you'd used me to get the $50,000, it was easy to run. Easy to hurt you.'' He found Sue Ann's scarred arm, brought the palm to his cheek and held it that way a moment; and she knew he was sorry he'd made the remark about her scars. ''You see, you're a strong woman, Sue Ann,'' he said, letting her hand go. "But you're full of strong emotions, too, and they bring back the feeling I can't cope, can't fix the hurts. I was almost relieved not to have to deal with the degree of emotions I saw in you. It was hell leaving you behind—I felt empty—but it was easier to deal with than emotional entanglements."

"Why'd you decide to miss the flight and hear me out?"

He gently cuffed her chin. "Because, you idiot, I'm in love with you."

She raised a skeptical brow.

He chuckled. "You don't let me slide, do you, Sourdough? Okay, the truth is, I was as afraid of this talk as you were, because I knew if I could believe in you again, I had to tell you the truth about myself. Joking around is my way of dealing with emotional conflict."

"But I love your sense of humor, Jerry. It somehow keeps the wolves from the door—the emotional ones."

"Laughter is good, all right. But the point is, I freeze up when other people need me the most. I'm afraid I'll let you down."

"You were there for me when I needed you. Every single time."

"But you don't know what it cost me!"

"Hey," she soothed, leaning briefly to lay her cheek against him. "I will from now on. You can work on toughing out emotional crises, and I can work on sharing decisions. We both need to work on trust." She glanced up at him. "What do you say? Do we have a partnership?"

His clear gray-green gaze held steady, a look that opened the depths of him to her. "On one condition," he said softly, taking her face in his hands and bending to trace her mouth.

"What condition is that?" she whispered.

"That you—" he trailed his lips over her face "—say my name—" and along her jaw to her ear "—as if you'll just die—" he rasped, nipping her lobe "—if I don't take you home and love you till dawn, right now, right this minute."

"Without your luggage?"

He did something wet and intimate to her ear, and his voice rumbled. "We'll fetch it tomorrow. Tonight we'll—"

She moaned on a slow exhale, and they laughed together.

She remembered the surprise she'd brought him. Leaning down, she picked up the package. "There are so many things I was saving for our first night at the cabin," she said. "The truth about the money, this gift, the 'I love you's.' But on the way out here today I recalled Serena's advice. 'It's people that count, Mama,' she said. 'Not things.' She's right. Fancy wedding rings don't prove stability or community acceptance. Trying to control all the variables in a relationship doesn't guarantee happiness. A cabin in the wilderness won't make our marriage secure. We'll do those things, Jerry. Working together."

He stared at her a moment, nodded. Then he said, "You raised a smart one, Sue Ann. Serena's a credit to you."

"And you to your mother, Jerry. Go on—" she handed him the present "—open it."

The sack fell to the carpet as he withdrew the gift and stared at it, his face flushing. "Lord, Sue Ann. My mother's silver frame."

She stepped to his side to admire the filigreed silver frame surrounding their wedding portrait. She and Jerry were a tall, mature couple standing in the stone entrance to the chapel, hands entwined, a tentative smile on her face and a radiant one on his.

"My mother would have loved this," he said, choked up. "As much as I do."

He hugged her. Sue Ann let it be brief so Jerry wouldn't feel fettered by emotion. Against his shoulder, she said archly, "Now don't go all mushy on me, Jerry. You know dealing with people's emotions makes me want to run off to the airport, catch a plane south."

He must have been in shock. He held her more tightly. Then he stood her off, grinned wide, and smacked a big kiss on her lips. "My saucy Sourdough," he drawled. "You ready for a business proposition, partner?"

She tilted her head. "Business?"

Taking her arm, he began to walk her toward the exit, his head bent close as he outlined how they might collaborate on establishing a consulting firm that specialized in finance and operations management. "With your contacts," he concluded, "we might even take on small projects for the government. Streamline systems. Save the taxpayers some money. What do you think?''

She stopped him by the door, gazing thoughtfully at him, thinking it would be rewarding to build something together. ''I like it,'' she said. Suddenly she stuck out her hand. ''It's a deal . . . partner.''

They shook hands. Chuckling, turning at the same moment, they slipped out into the biting breeze coming off the inlet.

Sue Ann was glad of the bracing wind; it snapped her out of her euphoria long enough to prepare for the reunion with Eric and Laura. It would be an important moment, because the successful weathering of a near-breakup would draw them all closer together. And besides, she thought, grinning . . . the wind blowing through her hair made Jerry look at her as if she were Wonder Woman, and at this moment, she felt he wasn't too far wrong.

LOOK FOR OUR FOUR FABULOUS MEN!

Each month some of today's bestselling authors bring
four new fabulous men to Harlequin American Romance.
Whether they're rebel ranchers, millionaire power brokers
or sexy single dads, they're all gallant princes—and
they're all ready to sweep you into lighthearted fantasies
and contemporary fairy tales where anything is possible
and where all your dreams come true!

You don't even have to make a wish...Harlequin American
Romance will grant your every desire!

Look for Harlequin American Romance wherever Harlequin
books are sold!

Silhouette
SPECIAL EDITION

SPECIAL EDITION

Stories of love and life, these powerful
novels are tales that you can identify with—
romances with "something special" added in!

Fall in love with the stories of authors such
as **Nora Roberts, Diana Palmer, Ginna Gray**
and many more of your special favorites—as
well as wonderful new voices!

Special Edition brings you
entertainment for the heart!

WAYS TO *UNEXPECTEDLY* MEET MR. RIGHT:

♡ Go out with the sexy-sounding stranger
your daughter secretly set you up with
through a personal ad.

♡ RSVP yes to a wedding invitation—soon
it might be your turn to say "I do!"

♡ Receive a marriage proposal by mail—
from a man you've never met....

These are just a few of the unexpected
ways that written communication
leads to love in Silhouette Yours Truly.

Each month, look for two fast-paced, fun and
flirtatious Yours Truly novels
(with entertaining treats and sneak previews
in the back pages) by some of your favorite
authors—and some who are sure to
become favorites.

YOURS TRULY™:
Love—when you least expect it!

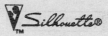

Arnold Schwarzenegger and Maria Shriver

Arnold and Maria met at a charity tennis tournament in Forest Hills, New York, in 1977. Nine years later Schwarzenegger married the TV journalist and Kennedy niece. Schwarzenegger himself is a conservative Republican, married into the Democratic Kennedy clan. His in-laws seem to take his outspoken, right-wing political views in stride.

At first, their careers caused them to be separated much of the time—she was on the East Coast and he on the West. Now, however, they have two daughters, so they are flying back and forth much less than they used to. Schwarzenegger sometimes has difficulty keeping his temper in check. He says, "I'll get in the car screaming about something and she'll say, 'Oh, yeah, looks good. Be brutal—look like the Terminator,' and I'll start laughing."

They had a traditional Roman Catholic ceremony at St. Francis Xavier Church.

B-ARNOLD